WORKING WITH CHRON

BASIC TEXTS IN COUNSELLING AND PSYCHOTHERAPY

Series Editor: Stephen Frosh

This series introduces readers to the theory and practice of counselling and psychotherapy across a wide range of topic areas. The books will appeal to anyone wishing to use counselling and psychotherapeutic skills and will be particularly relevant to workers in health, education, social work and related settings.

The books in this series are unusual in being rooted in psychodynamic and systemic ideas, yet being written at an accessible, readable and introductory level. Each text offers theoretical background and guidance for practice, with creative use of clinical examples.

Published

Jenny Altschuler
WORKING WITH CHRONIC ILLNESS

Paul Terry
COUNSELLING THE ELDERLY AND THEIR CARERS

Forthcoming

Sheila Ernst, Bill Barnes and Keith Hyde
AN INTRODUCTION TO GROUPWORK

Gill Gorell Barnes
COUNSELLING FAMILIES

Jan Wiener and Mannie Sher
COUNSELLING AND PSYCHOTHERAPY IN PRIMARY HEALTH CARE

Series Standing Order

If you would like to receive future titles in this series as they are published, you can make use of our standing order facility. To place a standing order please contact your bookseller or, in case of difficulty, write to us at the address below with your name and address and the name of the series. Please state with which title you wish to begin your standing order. (If you live outside the UK we may not have the rights for your area, in which case we will forward your order to the publisher concerned.)

Standing Order Service, Macmillan Distribution Ltd,
Houndmills, Basingstoke, Hampshire, RG21 6XS, England

WORKING WITH CHRONIC ILLNESS

A Family Approach

JENNY ALTSCHULER

With contributions by
Barbara Dale and John Byng-Hall

MACMILLAN

First published 1997 by
MACMILLAN PRESS LTD
Houndmills, Basingstoke, Hampshire RG21 6XS
and London
Companies and representatives
throughout the world

ISBN 0–333–62490–4

A catalogue record for this book is available
from the British Library.

This book is printed on paper suitable for recycling and
made from fully managed and sustained forest sources.

10   9   8   7   6   5   4   3   2
06 05 04 03 02 01 00

Printed and bound in Great Britain by
Antony Rowe Ltd, Chippenham, Wiltshire

To Sarah and Jack

CONTENTS

ACKNOWLEDGEMENTS

Over the course of my clinical work, I have been privileged to meet many families facing life-threatening and chronic illness who have had the courage to risk sharing their fears, hopes and practical struggles. It is these families I would first and foremost like to acknowledge. Details of all families discussed here have been significantly altered to ensure anonymity.

I would also like to thank my colleagues, members of the Tavistock Systems Team and Illness Research Project. Whilst writing this book, Barbara Dale and I have been involved in clinically-based research focusing on gendered patterns of caring in adult and parental relationships. Inevitably, much of that thinking is reflected here. Several of the families discussed were seen with Barbara Dale and Charlotte Burck, so that our shared clinical insights have informed the ideas presented in this book.

I would also like to thank Dr Dora Black, Dr Richard Trompeter and colleagues at the Royal Free Hospital for their support in paediatric liaison. Thanks to Dr David Katz and Dr John Launer for consultation on the medical conditions considered here, and to members of the Psychodynamic Approaches to Cancer Reading Group for sharing thoughts on the connections between systemic and pyschodynamic work. Thanks to Susan Altschuler, Gill Brace, Harriet Galgut, Helene Joffe, Jill Matus and Susan Lonsdale for their advice and discussion, and to Jackie Lemer for her careful reading of the typescript. Of course, particular thanks go to Stephen Frosh and Frances Arnold for suggesting I write this book, and their support over what has at times felt a long journey.

Finally my thanks go to my own family, for their flexibility and support while I've been writing. Particular thanks to David for his careful critique, proof reading and encouragement, and to our children, Gabriel and Marla, for reading the children's books recommended here, their computer consultation and good humour.

JENNY ALTSCHULER

Note: Feminine pronouns have been used throughout the text for the sake of simplicity, rather than using both masculine and feminine, when not referring to a specific person.

INTRODUCTION: THE CHALLENGE OF PHYSICAL ILLNESS

We live in an age of technological development: advances in medical technology have heralded enormous optimism in the treatment of illness, for families and professionals alike. However, increasingly we are having to recognise the tremendous emotional impact both illness and treatment can have on people's lives. A diagnosis of illness invariably evokes fears and anxieties about loss of functioning, changes in physical appearance, pain, discomfort, and separation from loved ones and peers through hospitalisation. Far from reducing the incidence of illness in our community, advances in acute care, together with the rise in the average age of the general population, have led to an *increase* in the prevalence of chronic illness.

For many, this means living with considerable uncertainty and restriction to their activities, having to attend countless appointments, and participate in painful, tiring medical procedures. Frequently, it means having to rely on the physical care of others. Views on health, illness and appropriate behaviour are inevitably influenced by those around us, by the ideas of professionals, family members and the wider social context in which we live. This introductory chapter explores ways in which current views of health and illness construct and determine our responses to illness, and our readiness to respect physiological signals and emotional distress both in ourselves and others.

Defining what illness means

It may be useful first to consider the distinctions between disease, illness and sickness. *Disease* is commonly viewed as referring to an objective biological abnormality, changes in the body that a physician treats. *Illness* refers to the more subjective experience of disease, the feelings associated with changes in bodily states. *Sickness* refers to the social and functional consequences that follow disease or illness, to a role justified on the basis of disease or illness. The focus therefore varies from the body (disease) to individual experience (illness) and society (sickness). However, these distinctions are far from clear. It is also possible to have a disease without feeling unwell, as with diabetes or undetected cancer, or to feel unwell without being recognised as ill, perhaps prior to diagnosis, or in pregnancy.

Societal attitudes have an impact on our preparedness to seek a diagnosis and readiness to adopt a sick role. We may feel ill but refuse to stop work. There may be magical thoughts that acknowledging illness could lead to a worsening of symptoms, or fears of the social consequences of such an acknowledgement, particularly where the condition carries a socially unacceptable stigma, such as AIDS.

Our families play an important role in determining beliefs and expectations about health and illness: how we define symptoms, an illness episode, its organisation and focus; what to say about physical well-being, decisions to seek care and perceptions of the care and medical care services provided (Ballenger and Alpert, 1989).

So-called objective factors, such as diagnoses, treatment and health-seeking behaviour, are themselves relatively subjective. Biomedical definitions and diagnoses vary in terms of gender (Waldron, 1983), location and social class (Whitehead, 1988). There are suggestions that what we regard as medical objectivity is but a collective, standardised story that has evolved over time in the attempt to provide structure and coherence in a field of diversity and confusion (Mold and Stein, 1986).

To understand then what we mean when we say someone is ill, or indeed disabled, we need to know *who* is making the statement, to *whom*, and *what* accounts for their interpretation. As the distinctions between disease, illness and sickness are far from clear, the term illness will largely be used here. The term will be used *when physical and emotional change tax bodily systems to the extent that an individual, or those she relates to, experience her as unwell and needing help.* Being labelled as ill, symptomatic or a patient means that a person is viewed differently by herself and others, setting in motion a particular type of relationship with professionals, families and friends. So, it is to these relationships that we turn in working with illness.

Health and illness: a narrow divide?

Health and illness have been described as two countries: if lucky, we live most of the time in the world of health, but all hold passports to the world of illness (Sontag, 1991). We know that symptoms beginning as minor ailments may indicate something more serious, and the media abounds with messages urging us to adopt health-inducing lifestyles. This dual citizenship defines our relationship to the world around us, to our families and society at large.

Rather than opposites, health and illness represent two poles of a continuum. The human body is not static, but in a constant state of change: the nervous system continually assesses new information and what changes are required to ensure we can survive, replace new cells and grow. This means dealing with changes in temperature, oxygen and energy levels, as well as responding to the multitude of bacteria ever present in our bodies. If our concept of a healthy body includes one that experiences fatigue, cold, and can be cut and bruised, what then do we label an illness?

Over time, illness has been variously described as destructive, a curse, punishment, liberator from life's trials, and even an occupation (Herzlich, 1984). Most of us take health for granted until we experience symptoms which question this state: we can rarely define health and illness clearly, but can usually say whether we regard ourselves as healthy or not. While feeling healthy or ill is a personal experience, concepts of health and illness are accumulated through a body of knowledge, specific to each culture. These concepts are profoundly influenced by our social and economic position (Cornwell, 1984), so that rates of diagnosis, prognosis and length of hospital stay tell us more about the social characteristics of any treatment system than about bio-medical processes (Waxler, 1981).

Definitions of health and illness influence the meanings we ascribe to being unwell and the behaviours we assume. These also range along a continuum, including aspects of the physical disease and how we relate to disease processes (Lee and Dwyer, 1995). Where there is limited physical damage, some of us make little shift in behaviour to accommodate to symptoms (the silent and healthy), while others alter their behaviour markedly (the worried well). Where there is considerable disease and damage, again, some refuse to take symptoms seriously (the stoics); while some become fully invested in being a patient. Any of these approaches may be destructive or helpful: failing to take symptoms seriously can result in physical damage and deterioration, while allowing life to become too circumscribed by illness can create problems for all family members.

So many factors contribute to decisions about adopting or rejecting illness roles: physical symptoms, their onset and likely outcome; individual variables, like threshold for stress, intellectual and emotional resources; family variables and adaptive style; all these influence how we interpret signals of danger. But while we are given the message of being able to heal ourselves, staying healthy or getting better is not only about personal responsibility: it relies on the care of others, on medical professionals and unpaid family members, particularly women.

The divide between health and illness becomes even more complex when we consider who we regard as ill. This book largely focuses on families where someone is regarded by herself or others as ill, where what is expected of her has significantly changed and where her body has become the object of others' concern, altering the relationship she has to herself. However, this includes not only people who have been diagnosed by a professional with labels like cancer, tuberculosis or renal failure, but those who have a known virus that has not yet emerged as an illness, as with the HIV virus; and those who experience themselves as unwell but for whom no organic cause has been found, as with some cases of post-viral infection and chronic pain.

All ill people have to integrate at least two descriptions of themselves, that of being a person in their own right and being ill. However, some in the latter group have to integrate a third description: of experiencing themselves as unwell but not being regarded as legitimately ill. This profoundly affects how they are treated by both family members and professionals. This is crucial, as the fit between the personal expectations and the expectations of others is what determines the readiness of individuals to give and receive the care so central to physical and psychological well-being.

Illness in a world defined by health

Clearly, being sick is far more than responding to biological phenomena: in addition to adopting a sick role, it involves relating to others who are healthy. Living with illness in a world of health influences views of how to be when ill, affecting our readiness to acknowledge suffering, to alter behaviour and receive care. An 'insider's' view of the world may be quite different from that of an 'outsider', with contradicting views about what good adjustment or coping well means. These different positions inevitably affect exchanges with people who have become 'patients', constraining interaction between ill people, professionals, families and friends. (Where possible, the word 'patient' is largely avoided here in a bid to challenge what this label means.)

Advances in medical practice mean that rules about life expectancy and quality of life are changing. Many conditions which were once considered incurable can be stabilised or cured. Retaining and balancing two dimensions of self concurrently then poses the central task of adjustment: a self as ill/disabled and a self able to engage in social activities. Integrating these dual aspects of self determines the relationship of an individual to the family, to society and the illness itself. Part of this includes the individual's relationship to the illness: there may be times when the pain, fatigue or discomfort means someone's primary relationship is to illness and pain rather than to people in their external world.

However, pain and discomfort are again not only about personal suffering but include the relationship with the person to whom symptoms are reported. Having to appear acceptable to the world of health and 'normality' can mean being restricted to structures that may not fit with the ill person's needs. It may also mean looking after the healthy, protecting others from the impact of their condition, sometimes to the detriment of personal health.

Chronic and acute conditions are viewed somewhat differently by the worlds of health and illness. When acutely ill, a person moves suddenly into a position of being a patient, with a legitimate right to a 'sick role'. This is often seen as less legitimate when chronically ill: other than on occasions which reinforce the claim of being ill, like medical consultations or during crises, people who experience themselves as unwell on a long-term basis are largely expected to manage their symptoms, within a world defined by the healthy.

Although the strategies used in these situations have much in common, they are rarely discussed outside self-help groups, as if the sense of shame in being ill means that the battle to manage symptoms has to be kept silent. As professionals, we cannot afford to overlook this secrecy and shame, how value judgements ascribed to being ill contribute to redefining identity, affecting the demands family members can make on one another.

Linking mind and body

Medical literature reflects diverse views on the connections between physical and psychological processes. Until the time of Descartes, medicine had a tradition of viewing the mind and body as inextricably linked. A split was then introduced between mind and body: medicine began to focus primarily on physical aspects of illness, while the mind was left to philosophers and psychologists. However, this division is no longer defensible: technology can now prolong life beyond the point when it has meaning for the patient, so that to separate physiological from psychological functioning makes little sense. While psychological functioning cannot be predicted purely on the basis of physiology, currently research suggests their interaction contributes to coping strategies and producing dysfunction (Hodes and Moorey, 1993), for example:

(a) physical factors affect psychological functioning through action to the brain, as with syphilis;
(b) psychological factors, like stress, intervene with physical functioning through physiological mechanisms, as with asthma;
(c) psychological factors induce behaviours that influence physical functioning, as with smoking;
(d) physical factors impact on psychological functioning through the meanings associated with it, as with conditions like AIDS.

Research highlights similar interaction between physiological and family functioning (Steinglass and Horan, 1988), considering how:

(a) families act as a resource, enhancing resistance to illness and determining compliance with treatment;
(b) family functioning contributes to the onset of the illness;
(c) illness impacts on family functioning;
(d) family behaviour and illness course mutually affect one another.

The power of metaphors and images

Whether diagnosed with a condition like cancer, AIDS or ME, reactions to illness relate not only to physical symptoms but also to the metaphors and images ascribed to each condition. Drawing on cultural and historical metaphors in literature, Sontag (1991) illustrated how tuberculosis is romantically portrayed as a gentle disease affecting good but poor people, while cancer is largely portrayed as an evil disease attacking the bad and rich. The word cancer is now used as a metaphor for any undesired growth, be they moral values or politics. The fear associated with AIDS too is undoubtedly linked to its association with images of promiscuity and perversity.

Some of the most prevalent metaphors and images organising clinical thinking are those of *war*, as in fighting or attacking diseased cells, blasting cells with radiotherapy, resistance and defence; *sports*, as in losing or winning; *technology*, as in feedback, input and efficiency; and *economics*, as in viewing patients as consumers and professionals as providers (Stein, 1990). These metaphors construct the experience of illness for both professionals and families: recovery or deterioration has been framed as losing or winning the fight; healing has been replaced by a war between antibodies and immune systems: the language of purchaser and provider has altered expectations of treatment facilities.

Elsewhere I (Altschuler, 1993) and others (Jacobus, Keller and Shuttleworth, 1990) have suggested that images associated with health and illness have a *gender* bias; masculinity tends to be associated with cure (through terms like mastery), and femininity with weakness and failure (for example, with menstruation being defined as a failure of procreation). These images are not 'just words', but are linked with disparities in health care in Britain: for example, in resources for treating heart disease amongst women (Petticrew, McKee and Jones, 1993). There has been similar criticism that research on women's health has concentrated on areas that most affect men's interests like childbirth, contraception and breast cancer (Bequaert Holmes and Purdey, 1992); and questions raised about the rationale of addressing health campaigns, like AIDS prevention campaigns, primarily to women as if the blame and responsibility for disease prevention lies within the power of one gender only. Often, concepts of men's health are seen as synonymous with body building, as reflected in the magazine *Men's Health*.

Although disparities may be more evident in some contexts than others, both consciously and unconsciously the images and metaphors of our art, literature and everyday speech powerfully influence interactions between all players in the health system (families as well as professionals).

Images of the part of the body affected

While the actual limb or organ affected gives some clues to the practical adjustments required, body parts and bodily functions have far deeper meanings for us all. Words like *heart, guts, stomach, head* and *breast* portray powerful emotions, determining how we view infection or damage to such organs and the detachment required in having to treat them. The mother of a child with a heart defect was distressed by seeing red hearts displayed on St Valentine's Day: to her, use of the word 'heart' to denote love seemed a cruel mockery when this was the very organ destroying the person she most loved.

Where breasts or genital areas are affected, the implications for gender identity and intimate relationships may be considerable. With breast cancer in particular, attempts to protect a sexual partner may make it difficult for the 'insider', the person who has the symptoms, and the 'outsider' to articulate or hear what the condition means for each person individually. This leaves partners with less opportunity to confront the changes they face, limiting opportunities for developing new styles of sexual intimacy.

While the image the organ evokes provides clues to demands faced, it can also be a useful clinical tool in confronting the implications of the condition. For example, focusing on the images of a 'working' and 'feeling' heart enables victims of heart attack to connect concretely with the emotions associated with their condition. This connection helps people reconstruct their understanding of their experiences and risk the change in lifestyle which is so crucial to rehabilitation (Wilde McCormick, 1988).

Socio-cultural meanings

We are all born into a socio-cultural reality. This alters over time, enabling us to make decisions, categorise our experiences and negotiate our understanding and expression of illness: research indicates that Jewish and Italian families tend to report symptoms freely, but Irish and British families minimise or conceal ailments (Zborowski, 1969). While concepts of health are largely based on the absence of illness in the West, in Japan the essential determinant is how long it takes to recover from illness (R. Hill, 1988). Both cultures place not only physical but moral value on remaining healthy. Chinese concepts of health appear to be more accepting of illness, emphasising the connection between mind, body and community: respect for the body meant that, until recently, operations were often shunned, and attempts were made to bury removed organs with the body at funerals. However, when a child becomes seriously ill, this acceptance may be less evident: a child's failure to perform essential ancestral rituals at a parent's funeral threatens the well-being of the community, so that childhood illness is problematic for the whole community. In addition, the family's connection to the wider community means that where illness is felt to be socially unacceptable, the level of shame experienced may be exacerbated.

Each socio-cultural group may view illness slightly differently. Where ill people come from a minority group, attempts at enlightenment have sometimes backfired: recognising alternative values has led to viewing difference as dangerous, as contributing to ill health and as a barrier to Western medicine. In many ways this is also true of attitudes to alternative medicine.

Just how we increase our capacity to encode or understand differences is complex: one option is to consult with colleagues from other ethnic groups, or read about other cultures. However, none of us can be accurately described in terms of adherence to a particular group: some immigrants hold on to beliefs dominant in their country of origin, others try to integrate these beliefs, while still others dispense entirely with traditional customs. Often, however, during illness, certain family members return to traditional values.

In multi-cultural Britain, resources are not always experienced as being equally available to all cultural, ethnic and religious groups. Whether this charge is valid or not, we need to ensure the promotion of health services is geared equally to all members of society.

Causal explanations: personal control, responsibility and blame

Having established that illness exists, we tend to try to explain what has happened. As we change from being healthy to ill, the meaning we attach to these terms alters, as do explanations of cause and blame. This means we face not only illness, but a change in how we understand and explain life events. While explanations tend to vary with family experience and social class, common themes have been noted.

At diagnosis, depending on the seriousness of the condition, early feelings of helplessness tend to be evoked, and patterns of defence are summoned as a means of protecting ourselves against collapse. One effect can be to *distance* ourselves from our own bodies: 'This isn't really me.' The illness is experienced as a breakdown of the body: the body becomes externalised and seen as an unreliable but indispensable vehicle, rather than an integral part of who we are.

Feelings of *blame* may not remain internalised: blaming others serves the purpose of dissolving fear and leaving a sense of control intact. In response to fear, anxiety and powerlessness, patients tend to blame society, society to blame health care, and health providers to blame patients. Locating illness outside ourselves dissolves the fear, leaving a sense of control intact. Throughout history, particularly when faced with incurable mass illnesses conditions, like the Black Plague, syphilis and (more recently) AIDS, people have responded by projecting responsibility for its origin and spread on to others, distancing themselves from the condition, it's 'not me', 'not my group'. This is as apparent in British society as abroad: in South Africa, blacks tend to blame white foreigners for the spread of AIDS (Joffe, 1994).

All too easily, this links with other targets of blame in society, leading to 'medical policing' (Foucault, 1975), to social institutions trying to monitor, regulate and subdue individuals in the name of health: industries and restaurants segregate smokers and non-smokers; drivers face prosecution for failing to use seat belts; and people who are HIV positive are currently barred from entering certain countries.

Beliefs that the onset and outcome of illness is the responsibility of the person afflicted stem from increased awareness of links between lifestyle and disease. However, they are often more accusations than explanations. Insensitive use of scientific enquiry can collude with society's wish to deny the reality of illness and death. Our society encourages us to think that the correct attitude of mind, diet or exercise gives us control over our bodies, to remain healthy and alive: attempts to identify the connection between Type A, B and C personalities with heart attack and cancer risk mean that in becoming ill, people have to recognise not only that they are ill, but that they are responsible for failing to fight disease. This ignores the complexity of disease processes, how economic and environmental factors shape the risks we are exposed to. Many links to health impairment are only statistical and do not directly prove that illness can be linked to risky or indulgent behaviour.

Accusations of personal blame are more readily applied to adults than children: rather than holding children accountable for their own health, parents are blamed. I would not want to minimise the control parents have over children's well-being; however, depicting parents as incompetent in this way suggests that they should do better, and have the capacity to do so, ignoring the lack of resources and information often faced. So, when a child is ill and may die, parents have to confront not only the illness but also accusations of having failed to provide the care and protection their children needed.

We could argue that processes of blaming disempowered members of society contributes to how men and women apportion blame: men tend to assume an external cause for illness, while women tend to blame themselves. 'Mother-blaming', so prevalent in psychological literature, may account for why health campaigns are invariably targeted at women and mothers rather than men (Blaxter, 1983).

As yet, society has not found a less blaming way of formulating the experience of illness. As professionals, it is crucial that we consider how explanations of illness influence our interactions. Locating responsibility in one part of a family system, whichever it is, influences how the blamed person relates to the illness and the ill person: parents who feel responsible for causing their child's illness may try to distance themselves from the child, becoming less able to help that child face the illness than those who do not feel blamed.

Psychological resilience in facing uncertainty

Adaptation to the discovery of illness demands radical reorganisation of individual and family life. Confronted with a life-threatening diagnosis, each family member has to find a way of redefining their expectations of themselves and their relationships to one another. Adults and children who have previously adjusted well may struggle enormously in the face of illness. While I would in no way want to minimise the horrors faced by each family, it is important to recognise too that, despite the common-sense view that stressful events are damaging, many people show unexpectedly robust adaptations, and find resources they were previously unaware of. Several studies dispute the assumption that families facing illness exhibit greater levels of emotional disturbance than those who are physically healthy (Spaulding and Morgan, 1986; Perrin and McLean, 1988). Until recently, there has been little acknowledgement of what may be gained: an increased capacity for compassion, sensitivity, understanding, the sense of competence that evolves from nurturing others, and a rekindling of intimacy in families (Ferrari, 1984; Horwitz and Kazak, 1990).

Of late, there has been a shift in the focus of research, moving from risk factors to mechanisms mediating and negotiating risk: to considering what reduces the impact of adversity and probability of chain reactions developing where children face a range of potentially difficult situations (Garmezy and Masten, 1994), parental divorce or marital conflict (Jenkins and Smith, 1990), ill health (Antonovsky, 1979), and diabetes in particular (Blechman and Delamater, 1993).

Such a change has required considering how, irrespective of life events, we all negotiate contradictions in our everyday lives: some experiences enhance our sense of coherence and who we are, while others are more challenging and require profound redefinition of who we are. How we balance these contradictions, acts as a protective mechanism when facing trauma.

Overwhelmingly, studies suggest that crucial to dealing with emotional trauma is access to:

(a)   confirming relationships;
(b)   an area of competence;
(c)   the opportunity for self-reflection (Beardslea, 1989).

These studies highlight the value of establishing which aspects of the experience are the most traumatic, and how family members, professionals and members of the community serve as a resource in times of trauma.

A range of coping mechanisms and strategies has been noted in response to illness. Some people tend to try to alter what they do in difficult circumstances (problem-based coping); others tend to minimise the emotional impact through adopting a particular attitude (emotion-based coping: see Lazarus and Folkman, 1984); and many use a combination of styles in encountering stressful events.

Diagnosis in particular acts as an assault on what is known: many talk of a sense of *rupture*, that their entire world view is shattered: assumed sequences of events and relationships are thrown out of order, family relationships take on a temporal quality and the present becomes discontinuous with both past and future time (Cohen, 1993). Managing this uncertainty involves redefining personal stories, developing *strategies* to manipulate what is known, unknown or unknowable. These may include trying to block out uncertainty by covering up; minimising pain; and disguising the extent of incapacitation or how out of control the body feels.

Within families, certain strategies may not always feel equally appropriate to all. Some prefer to discover as much as possible about the illness, but not everyone wants to know all that is known: many prefer to live with uncertainty, particularly when a condition is feared to be terminal. This sense of uncertainty may pervade all aspects of life: how we *address social interactions*, like deciding who and when to tell about the condition, how we *face the possibility of physical risk* in children's play, and adjustments to our concept of *time*. Some adopt a 'day by day' strategy, avoiding thinking about the future unless triggered by key words, like New Year or birthdays. This is easily thrown into disarray: in a family where the father had cancer, his 4-year-old daughter said he had not been to school since the tadpoles turned into frogs. Until then, the parents had tried to live in the present and face each day as it came. The daughter's comment reminded them of the passing of time and the unpredictable future, confronting them with their overwhelming uncertainty.

Focusing on coping strategies and resilience in no way implies reducing support services: this could but add to the burden families face. But it does mean we need to re-assess what is protective and helpful to ensure our interventions are experienced as strengthening rather than de-skilling.

Psychosocial models of illness

As professionals, what we seek from theory is a framework to promote our capacity to work with the uncertainty of illness, a framework that enables us to help people face what may be a complex, frightening and long-term process. This section is far from comprehensive, but seeks to provide some insights into the major theoretical approaches informing work with illness.

Psychodynamic theory

Psychodynamic theory has played a considerable role in the understanding of illness, both in seeking to understand the development of illness, and in therapy with people who are ill. The theory is rooted in the belief that health can be influenced by emotions: early work examined the psychological conflicts and personality traits responsible for the emotional states contributing to the development of disease. Although Freud was curious about mental processes underlying the somatic symptoms of hysteria, he urged colleagues to resist linking emotions too readily with endocrinology and the automatic nervous system.

However, complex theories of causality were developed. Intrapsychic conflicts were assumed to evoke intense emotions producing arousal in the autonomic system, leading to pathological changes in the structure and function of vulnerable body parts (Alexander, 1950; Deutch, 1959). The idea that neurotic behaviour is a risk factor for disease gained prominence. While some empirical support has been found for a disease-prone personality, linking illness with the tendency to show marked depression, anger, hostility and anxiety, how these are necessarily associated with internal conflicts remain unclear. Currently, there is little empirical evidence that therapy can reverse or alleviate physical symptoms.

More recent work draws on advances in bio-medical research, exploring how diseases may be caused by multiple factors rather than one cause. For example, there are suggestions that verbal and non-verbal emotional behaviour contribute to regulating biological systems. The hypothesis is that disease occurs when someone is unable internally to regulate distressing feelings, like the helplessness and hopelessness aroused following a disruption in important attachment relationships (Taylor, 1992).

Clinical work is based on the assumption that *the way in which anyone reacts is influenced by the internalised, intrapsychic impact* of the illness on a family member or professional: intellectual concepts and reactions cannot exist without corresponding or conflicting internal fantasies. Therapy or consultation involves attending to the behaviour between that person and the professional, the speech, mood and play of their interaction. This includes sharing and integrating aspects not accessible to the conscious mind and relies on both *counter-transference*, awareness of the impact of the work on the therapist, and *transference*. Transference refers to internalised feelings and impulses of the patient left over from earlier relationships that are transferred or directed to those in the here and now, be this a therapist or other professional staff. This may include interpreting and accessing how defences of control or splitting protect someone from the pain of the illness or disability but prevent more effective mourning, which could enable feelings to be reworked or re-evaluated. For example, drawing on the concepts of good and bad internal objects in her work with ill children, Judd (1989) describes how the pain of thirst, hunger and not being held can be experienced as persecutory: pain is expelled from a source with which the child has an active relationship, a 'good object', to a so-called 'bad object', in order to preserve the 'good breast' for nourishment and comfort. When ill, attempts to get rid of pain involve 'projecting' it on to the outside world. However, where long treatment is required, good objects including parents, spouses and trusted clinicians are expected to intervene with painful and intrusive procedures, so that maintaining the split between good and evil becomes problematic, threatening the child's sense of coherence.

While much of this work focuses on individuals, these ideas have also been applied to groups and professional systems, for example Balint's work with General Practitioners (1957), and Menzies Lyth's work with nurses (1957). The latter described how nurses' feelings of helplessness, rage and disgust reflect punitive and unconscious fantasies of infancy, which can be fired by the violent fantasies of the patient or family.

While this work has been tremendously influential, focusing on intrapsychic phenomena has meant paying less attention to interactions in the here and now. Several therapists have stressed the importance of *accommodating* their work in these circumstances. They emphasise the need for caution: as catastrophic anxiety may be present, the protective nature of defences should be respected and not challenged too harshly. This does not mean ignoring what is painful, but pacing carefully how and when to help name what feels unnameable (Emmanuel, 1990).

Attachment theory

Rather than formulating a method of working with illness, attachment theory provides a framework for analysing some of the difficulties presented, particularly the potential disruption to the development of security. This has had a powerful influence on hospital policy, particularly for ill children. Outlining how relationships with the external world affect the development of attachment and security in the young child (Bowlby, 1988), the theory notes that attachment is mediated by the sound, sight and touch of a so-called attachment figure. To be securely attached means to feel safe, while insecure attachment involves mixed emotions of loss, depression and rejection.

When faced with a threat, like illness, people tend to seek out an attachment figure from whom they can obtain relief. Only then can they feel free to move away and explore. In a context of crisis and uncertainty, ongoing access to attachment figures is crucial to enable children and adults to adapt to their changing situation. An early film (Bowlby and Robertson, 1952) exploring the effects of separation on young children markedly influenced hospital policy in Britain, increasing the provision for contact between hospitalised young children and adults. The value of continuity of professional care-givers has also been highlighted: as being ill easily evokes unmet dependency needs, both medical and non-medical professionals can become important substitute attachment figures at these times.

Hence, this approach has affected attitudes to care. With few exceptions (Byng-Hall, 1995), however, this work has focused on mother-child interaction, with less focus on attachment to other family members, and not much attention paid to disrupted attachments when siblings or parents are ill.

Cognitive theory

This approach has primarily been used to explain health-related behaviour, providing guidelines for preventative interventions. This relies on an understanding that behaviours and emotions are intimately linked with beliefs about the world: while beliefs influence responses, they are rarely questioned; they lie beyond normal awareness, but are not unconscious. Beliefs may be appropriate, false, dysfunctional or in need of change. Not all false beliefs demand change, and false does not imply dysfunctional: denying the seriousness of an illness, a false belief, may increase chances of survival.

Therapy aims to help people *identify the relationship between cognitions, emotions and behaviours* to increase their awareness of what are seen as dysfunctional cognitions, and alter these. This means linking beliefs, commonly used thinking errors, emotions and behaviours. *Negative automatic thoughts* are signalled when a person experiences a change in mood. Therapy involves identifying dysfunctional beliefs through examining the themes that trigger automatic thoughts. They may be enhanced and perpetuated by distortions to thinking and appraisal: for example, patients may focus on only one part of their memory of a diagnostic consultation, the negative aspects, even though other parts contradict this. *Habitual thinking* increases vulnerability to hearing certain information: someone whose usual style of thinking is 'all or nothing', may think they are at death's door when told they are not 100 per cent well.

The approach is primarily *educational*, with the understanding that this insight will extend to future events. It has been used across a wide range of conditions, including altering behaviour in patients prone to heart disease (Friedman *et al.*, 1986), with rheumatoid arthritis (Applebaum *et al.*, 1988) and with cancer patients (Tarrier and Maguire, 1984) and in the control of pain (Turk and Fernandez, 1991).

While the approach is clear and has helped identify variables for change, seeking primarily cognitive or rational explanations and minimising emotions and motivation has been somewhat counter-productive. For example, preventative work has relied on actual behaviour rather than the intentions or interactional processes determining decisions (Abraham and Sheeran, 1993). It remains to be seen whether the optimism and considerable financial invest-ment engendered by this approach has been repaid.

Systemic theory

As the value of describing relationships between family members and professionals as systems forms the main framework of this book, this section comments only on broad concepts. Primary assumptions of systemic work are that: any major event affecting an individual in a system impacts on the relationship between all other members of that system; there is a connection between beliefs and behaviours; change may be addressed at the level of belief or behaviour; change to any one part of the system has a 'ripple' effect on other parts of the system. This chapter has addressed how beliefs prevalent in the context of an individual, family or professional influence responses to illness. In work with individuals, families or professional networks, this means considering how individual reactions are influenced by the responses and expectations of others, and how the fit between the beliefs and expectations of members of a system influence responses to any situation. As any situation changes, so too does the style an individual or family adopts.

This model is being increasingly used in clinical work with families, in addressing the fit between family members and profes-sionals. Most usually, attempts are made to work with as many members of the system impacting on the individual as possible. However, this is not always possible but, even when working individually, the focus remains primarily on interpersonal relation-ships rather than on internal or intrapsychic phenomena. Focusing on how individual behaviour is both linked to, but not fully determined by, context provides a less non-pathologising frame-work of conceptualising problems in coping with illness.

Anecdotal self-report

Finally, in exploring current models of illness, we cannot ignore self-reports, the anecdotal stories of people who have personal experi-ence with illness. Books like *Diary of a breast* written by a woman with breast cancer (Segrave, 1995), *Cancer in Two Voices* co-written by partners about facing cancer (Butler and Rosenblum, 1994), and *And when did you last see your Father?* about a son's understanding of his father's cancer (Morrison, 1993) are but a few of the brave and important testimonies of personal struggles with illness. They provide crucial insight to work within this field and contribute forcibly to our clinical thinking.

Conclusions

This chapter considers the challenge presented by physical illness to both family members and professionals, outlining dominant constructs informing our work. In so doing, what was stressed was the importance of extending our understanding of illness beyond the context of the individual, to the wider contexts of the family and professional systems.

How we respond, both as professionals and family members, is determined by the story we evolve about our own experience, stories constructed by factors like physical symptoms, individual characteristics and attitudes, families and professional networks. This affects the fit between our own and others' stories of illness, be they family members or health-care professionals. This fit determines how people retain a sense of self that both includes the illness, but is not totally consumed by it. This 'fit' between the beliefs and understanding of families facing illness and the services provided must be considered to ensure that we do not add to the processes of de-skilling or pathologising so commonly reported.

As clinicians and researchers, we need to examine whether current constructs aid or limit the flexibility of adults, children and professionals in dealing with uncertainty and change. This may mean reformulating stories of illness, so that conditions such as cancer, AIDS or renal failure can be seen not as a punishment, failure, embarrassment or curse but as illnesses.

Summary

1. While being unwell is a personal experience, the meaning attached to this by others impacts on the experience of illness, influencing attitudes to self-care and contact with professionals. As members of a system which is focused on illness, both families and professionals play a major role in determining this experience.

2. *Disease* has been defined as referring to an objective biological abnormality, *illness* to the more subjective experience of being unwell, and *sickness* to the social and functional consequences that follow being labelled ill. However, distinctions are far from clear. Research highlights variability in diagnoses, treatment and health-seeking behaviour across location and social class.

3. Distinctions between the terms *health* and *illness* are also far from clear. Definitions vary according to socio-cultural groupings and who defines these terms. We can be positioned on health and illness dimensions simultaneously.

4. *Metaphors* and *images* of illness vary with socio-cultural grouping and the body part affected, powerfully influencing interactions between family members and health-care providers.

5. The meanings we attach to illness and caring are influenced by *gender*, and influence the provision of services, financing of medical research and assumptions of roles.

6. Living with illness in a *world largely defined in terms of health* means that people afflicted with illness have to accommodate to the healthy, affecting how different members of a family understand what is wanted or needed at any one time.

7. Focusing on *deficit* only limits our understanding of what may also be gained through illness, limiting more appropriate provision of resources.

8. A range of theoretical approaches were outlined, placing emphasis on their particular contribution to work with illness, namely the psychodynamic, attachment, cognitive and systemic models.

9. What cannot be overestimated is the importance of ensuring that the services provided meet the needs of families and avoid adding to the burden of what is faced.

2

UNDERSTANDING THE IMPACT OF ILLNESS ON HEALTH-CARE SYSTEMS

Illness imposes grief, loss and change on so many areas of life: children and adults may have to undergo painful or scarring treatment, take large doses of medication or spend long periods attached to complex machinery, altering their body image and sense of autonomy. They may have to balance emotions of fear and hope, both for themselves and for those on whom they find themselves temporarily or permanently dependent. Uncertainty makes it difficult to know what is safe to express and share with others.

As professionals, this work confronts us with people facing unpredictability and ambiguity, people who are questioning and redefining the meaning of their lives. As family therapists, psychologists, social workers, teachers, doctors or nurses, we too may struggle with what to say or do. We may question our roles, and be afraid of adding to their burden by conducting painful, intrusive medical procedures, or by talking with adults and children about illness.

Any professional, medically trained or not, faces a daunting and challenging task: to help the ill person and family accept treatment and manage a situation of ongoing uncertainty in a way that does not leave them feeling de-skilled and helpless. How we manage this will be influenced by our wide-ranging views on professional care in medical contexts. Both medical and non-medical professionals may have concerns that the intimacy of care required in this emotionally laden context could cloud objectivity and overcome professional restraint. Alternatively, we may find our technical knowledge creates unhelpful distance and aloofness in relating to patients and colleagues. As medically trained professionals in particular, what is most difficult is that, despite advances with certain illnesses, the brief for treatment of so many conditions has to be framed as providing palliative care or symptom relief, rather than cure.

As such, this work can have a profound effect on us personally, confronting us with the need to re-evaluate the limits of our training and expertise, beliefs about normality, childhood and expectations of families, personal responsibility and efficacy. Our relationships and support systems outside work, personal health, previous experiences and beliefs about illness and loss influence how we manage this, and will be explored more fully later (Chapter 8). However, equally important are interactions with colleagues in our current work settings. A particularly effective framework for understanding this work is viewing patterns of relationships between patients, professionals and families as a network of systems, each affecting and being affected by the other.

Systems theory in the context of health care

Systems thinking originated about 50 years ago. Scientists noticed that a wide variety of biological and non-biological phenomena share the attributes of systems. They began to explore functional and structural rules valid for describing all systems: rules about how systems are organised, maintained, process information, and adapt to change. The term system is now used to describe the relationship between members of any unit, such as a paediatric unit or family group.

While the whole unit is different from the sum of its parts, change to any one part inevitably affects the rest of the system.

Change at one level can result in change at another. For example, changes in behaviour can influence beliefs. Anyone working with illness will be familiar with the idea of the body operating as a system, where what happens to one part of the body affects all other parts: an injury to the knee influences the way a person stands and walks, and is likely to have an effect on the back and whole bone structure. This in turn limits the ability to carry out strenuous activity, influencing one's sense of self, and beliefs about personal competence.

How does a system work?

One way of understanding how systems work is to examine *feedback loops* in interactional processes. In any feedback loop, A affects B, B affects C , C affects D and D affects A. These loops operate at all levels of human interaction, from the cellular to the social and political, and involve both verbal and non-verbal communication. This means that actions we commonly regard as causes can more accurately be redefined as arbitrary punctuations in a complex of interacting cycles.

Viewing actions in this circular way can free us to think differently. In a medical consultation, for example, rather than seeing or blaming a response (such as an angry outburst) on the character of either patient or doctor, we seek to understand the actual context of interaction in which it occurs. The behaviour of doctor and patient, their tone of voice and physical contact, influences the behaviour of the other, in turn affecting patterns of relating between the two.

This means that we cannot view the behaviour of two people in isolation from other relationships within the setting, with other professionals, family members and friends. These relationships continually influence perceptions of one another, affecting subsequent interactions. So, as professionals, we are inevitably affected by the actions, beliefs and encounters with colleagues and families.

It is worth focusing on three core concepts in particular. Systems thinking assumes that *what we observe around us can be understood in different ways*: events can be seen in different contexts or at different levels of meaning. For example, angry criticism of a nurse by parents for delaying feeding a child can be labelled as anger if we think of that response in isolation. At another level, that same response can be seen as part of a wider, more inclusive process that takes into account past experiences, such as the parents inability to find a cure for their child's fatal illness. Embedded in this systemic process, we can understand the parents' response as a reaction to their sense of incompetence and failure.

Second, systemic thinking implies an appreciation that *there is a connectedness between the person's beliefs and behaviour*: as patients and professionals, we behave as we do because we believe we are doing the best thing in those circumstances. Many factors influence beliefs about appropriate behaviour, but are not always shared. For example, that angry response by parents might relate to differences in beliefs between nurse and parents about their respective roles when a child is ill. How they negotiate their difference will be influenced by the 'fit' between these two systems of belief.

Third, systemic thinking requires an appreciation that *the observer is inevitably part of the system*: whatever is observed is affected by the interaction between the observer and other points in the system.

Therefore, doctors or counsellors might pause to consider that their description of the nurse or parent's response will reflect their own constructions. Their view will be based on interaction on the unit, training, background and dealings with people in the past. Viewing our position as observers in the system may help us to remain non-judgemental and avoid siding with one person in such an encounter.

How do systems deal with entries and exits?

Medical care systems, like biological systems, have a fragile balance which can be altered by change or stress to any components, including change in a patient's condition, or shifts in the commitment of a patient's family or friends. Entries and exits, like changes in staffing, a patient dying or even leaving a unit on recovery, involve not only loss but changes to the existing hierarchy and alliances on the unit. Any such change alters the structure of the system. So difficulties are more likely to arise around times of transition, serving to delay, reverse or shape the new patterns of relationships. Inevitably, the unit continually balances the need for change with that of stability and predictability.

Systems appear to respond to disturbances by attempting to re-establish the previous status quo, protecting the system from chaos and disintegration. This has been called homeostasis, or first order change. However, they have the capacity to alter their rules or structures to establish a new organisation appropriate to the changed circumstances: this is called second order change. For example, on a ward where the rule is that you respond to difficulties by carrying on and appearing unaffected by loss or pain, staff may react to a failed transplant by feeling tired, listless and lacking in concentration. Senior staff may point out that performance has dropped, encouraging staff to re-adopt previous styles of work (first order change). An alternative response (second order), is to help that group express is frustrations, pain and anger about the failed transplant, altering a ward rule about relating.

The way in which relationships are redefined may produce gains for some and losses for others. New rules inevitably reflect who in the hierarchy holds both formal and unacknowledged executive power. This vesting of power may be related to professional status and age, or even race and gender.

What does membership of a system mean?

Systems are not static entities: they may be closed or open with permeable boundaries to incorporate new members. Sub-systems develop, organised around specific tasks. For example, to address a child's fear of needles, a psychologist, doctor, nurse, parent and child may form a sub-system to deal with the task at hand. Once the phobia has been addressed, the group dissolves and members regroup according to membership of other groups. In this way, sub-groups form temporary or permanent alliances, ultimately affecting the wider system of which they are a part. The 'fit' between beliefs of members of the sub-system, and the expectations of the wider systems to which we belong (such as the psychiatric or paediatric teams), determine how these sub-groups operate.

What is the position of an individual in a system?

While it is useful to look at professional networks as systems, systems are made up of individuals. Personal beliefs can become incorporated into the belief system of the unit or team, influencing how others see reality and choose to act. On joining a team, a nurse, doctor or social worker is given a role through which the team's tasks are carried out. As new members, we can both influence and be influenced by the unit's expectations of our roles. Again, how we behave will be influenced by the 'fit' between our beliefs about the role and those of the organisation, beliefs about efficiency, autonomy, morality, loyalty and respect for hierarchy.

While we are all important to the functioning of a unit, we occupy different levels of overt and covert power. Relative positions of power are determined by such factors as the status of our positions outside the unit, salaries, officially recognised areas of responsibility and autonomy. At the same time, positions are simultaneously determined by informal power structures, by culture, race, class, disability and gender. These may or may not fit with the overt power structures, altering our sense of power or powerlessness within the unit.

Shared notions of power reflect dominant beliefs. In a medical system where most senior posts are still held by people who are white and/or male, race and gendered beliefs influence our understanding of professional relationships and organisational structure, determining the actions we take in any situation. Therefore, when we want to understand why a person behaves in a certain way, we must understand not only the relationships affected by that action, but the impact this has on belief systems.

Thinking about our own positions, we all have areas where we perform relatively autonomously, and others in which we are more constrained in what we are allowed to do. Some, but not all, of this will be written into our job descriptions. Again, we tend to perform most effectively where there is a fit between what is specified and what we feel we can accept to be part of the unit. If we act too autonomously, we may become disengaged from the unit, while if too constrained, our readiness to respond creatively can be inhibited (Campbell, Draper and Huffington, 1991). However, in medical teams, members are required both to adhere to strict constraints of practice and yet be able to respond flexibly when unpredictable crises arise. Misunderstandings can develop, requiring re-assessment of rules about roles and job descriptions.

At times, it may be useful to consider the following questions.

1. How do I describe the problem?
2. Why has the problem arisen now?
3. Who is most concerned about what is happening?
4. What does that person have to gain or lose from change?
5. What are the beliefs within the system about change?
6. How do the areas of constraint and autonomy clash with job descriptions?
7. How might the problem be related to race, gender, class or culture?
8. How do my views reflect my position within the unit?

As our understanding of any system is inevitably affected by our own position within the system, when difficulties arise it may be useful to consider recruiting the services of someone outside the unit as a consultant.

Interface between systems in health care

Medical advances and policy changes are creating ripple effects in health-care delivery, as we change from hospital- to community-based care, from provider- to client-focused services, and from illness- to preventative-centred services. With this there has been a shift in clinical practice, with a movement towards new specialisms and multi-disciplinary teams, the latter serving to restore the global nature of individuals, in biological, emotional, cognitive and relational terms.

In Britain today, health care is shared between the private and public sectors. Demographic trends, advances in technology, rising expectations of public health and commitment to community care has placed considerable pressure on the National Health Service (NHS). This has led to changes in funding public health and restructuring services, increasing competition between hospitals and general practices with the split of services into 'purchasers' and 'providers'. Whilst this book will not focus on these transitions, at the time of writing widely disparate beliefs about the gains and losses of this restructuring are affecting relationships between staff at all levels of the health system.

Current health care can be roughly divided into three levels, allowing for referral between the levels.

1. *Primary care* teams generally provide the first link for patients and families to health care and treat 80–90 per cent of all healthcare problems.
2. Where medical problems require specialised help, *secondary care* is recruited. This may include referrals to orthopaedic surgeons, cardiologists, ophthalmologists and family therapists.
3. *Tertiary care* settings provide specialised treatment in highly specified areas such as childhood cancer or intractable anorexia nervosa.

Differences between levels are not always as clear cut: General Practitioners (GPs) often undertake care that could also be addressed at another level. While this allows a more holistic approach to health care, it can raise questions about roles in family-professional systems: for example, in attending to importance of the family in prevention, rehabilitation and treatment management, how do GPs deal with conflicts of interests in caring for individuals and families, and how does this impact on relationships with patients. This does not imply that such initiatives are unhelpful, but emphasises that any such changes to working styles influence both families and professionals.

Negotiating differences between medical and non-medical professionals

Recognising limitations of the mind-body split in health care has resulted in increased collaboration, altering communication and trust between professionals: a wide range of non-medical professionals, including psychologists, speech and occupational therapists, social workers and teachers have joined medical professionals in patient care. In both inpatient and outpatient settings, multi-disciplinary team members are likely to have somewhat different beliefs about professional style in patient care, fostered by training, personal experiences and beliefs. This may include differences in:

- what information to share with patients and their families;
- the length of time patients are seen;
- perceptions of whether services should be provided around the clock or in scheduled sessions;
- whether technical or colloquial language is most helpful;
- the use of direct advice;
- whether to consult patients and families about decisions;
- use of family and individual history;
- levels of confidentiality, and attitudes to expressing emotions.

In the medically defined setting of inpatient settings, the demands of the illness inevitably take priority and emergencies frequently arise requiring tremendous *flexibility*. So, when misunderstandings and differences in expectations emerge, they may be difficult to address. For example, I recall having found it extremely frustrating when blood tests that were not emergencies had been booked into times of family therapy sessions. It is, of course, feasible that disregarding pre-booked sessions related to *ambivalence* about trusting another professional. However, quite practically, I learned that my medical colleague did not carry a personal diary: her expertise relied on the ability to act spontaneously, so she was accustomed to booking procedural interventions without having to consider pre-arranged appointments. This example highlights the importance of finding a forum in which such practical issues can be clarified to preserve a working relationship that both recognises the need for flexibility and respects the boundaries of appointments where possible.

From my own experience, I know there have been times, as when a patient's condition deteriorates and urgent medical treatment is needed, that lack of a medical training has left me, as a non-medical professional, with feelings of helplessness and inadequacy. However, paradoxically, it is this very freedom from medical responsibility that can enable us as non-medical professionals to address the emotional impact of the illness and prove most useful to multi-disciplinary teams. Rules about working styles reflect the professional status of staff. In a medically-defined system, the views of non-professionals may not always be heard and often need to be stated more clearly and confidently in order to be valued. Comments about emotional needs and physical surroundings of treatment are enormously important to patient care, ensuring that individuals and their families are recognised as people rather than disease entities.

However, as non-medical professionals, we need to familiarise ourselves with the illness, treatment procedures and likely prognosis, so that we recognise when changes in mood or emotional expression relate to the illness or treatment, or the value of organising appointment times around chemotherapy sessions. Whether we choose to glean information from medical colleagues, or from the families themselves, this is essential to helping people reflect on their experience and face the feelings evoked by their illness. Some of these fears may be widely shared, such as 'Will I ever become my old self?', but others may be specific to certain conditions, like fears about growth retardation, delayed puberty with renal failure and prospects of conception.

The dynamics of referral

Referral provides a useful illustration of interaction between systems. We all occupy a certain position within the health-care system. Attitudes and beliefs are affected by membership of professional groups, determining our salaries, roles, support network, access to other professional groups and range of responsibility. Although we may broadly agree on the nature of a referral, we usually have different views on appropriate interaction between ourselves, colleagues, patients and family members.

To maximise the fit between referrer and referee, it is important to clarify:

- expectations of the work;
- how the referral can be explained to the family;
- the level of communication appropriate to ensuring professionals can share important information and changes;
- respect for different rules of confidentiality;
- differences in role, expertise and time available.;

This is essential to avoid unhelpful splits developing, as can occur when a family is faced with different views from two or more professionals, where choosing one view means negating the other. Collaboration at referral is essential to ensure differences in expectations are addressed. These may be set up formally, using recognised channels of communication, or informally, on the telephone.

The referrer often occupies a particular position in the system (Selvini Palazzoli et al., 1980). For example, a GP may play an important role in the family, so that referral to a paediatrician or psychologist is viewed by the family (and possibly even by the GP) as a failure, rather than an achievement. Where the referrer is likely to maintain continuity of care, this needs to be recognised at the outset, to ensure the patient is able to take up the referral and the referrer is not left feeling de-skilled.

However, difficulties may arise for quite different reasons. Medical personnel, particularly physicians, perform a task that is highly valued in society. This status is recognised by salary, cultural prestige and associated power. Envy and competition can block effective collaboration, limiting the opportunity of patients and families to use the resources available. Issues such as differences in hours of work, freedom from medical responsibility and freedom to take leave at times like Christmas accentuate this difference, challenging relationships between staff in a complex environment.

All too easily, positions of authority can be abused. On inpatient units, where teams include a wide range of disciplines of varying levels of authority, professionals may find themselves in situations when they have been unable to avert the deleterious course of an illness. The sense of grief, failure and anger aroused can be overwhelming. At these times, careful attention to communication is required to avert a process of blaming one another or the patient for the powerlessness that is beyond anyone's control. Opportunities for collaboration, role clarity, respect for differences and a clear organisational structure can play an important part in avoiding difficulties escalating.

Styles of collaboration

Multi-professional and community-based practices are emerging and providing new models of health care. However, in working across levels and between professional groupings there may be different expectations about referrals and collaboration. For example, there may be differences in expectations of collaborating on referrals for family therapy or, say, gastro-enterology. Similarly, a family therapist may be unaware of how having to remain 'on call' impacts on the availability of medical colleagues. While clarifying expectations is important, finding a way of operating that fits within the framework of other referrals but does not compromise therapy is crucial.

In a hospital setting, the family interacts with several treatment systems. If the aim is for collaboration, participants of each system have to accommodate their behaviour to others. When any two systems meet, the behaviour of the new system is determined by how the structure of those systems fit: this is called structural coupling (Maturana and Varela, 1988). The term 'co-evolution' is used to describe the way in which each system has a continuous effect on its environment in its evolution, and is in turn affected by this environment.

Work across levels of medical systems can be seen as conversations across the boundary of systems, through which new systems evolve. In a medically defined system, all participants do not have equal power: only some participants have responsibility for admissions. However, for both sides to gain something from any encounter, they have to open their boundaries to render reflexive discussions possible. This process of co-evolving as a new, albeit temporary system is central to describing the interaction between several treatment systems, as well as their interaction with families.

Co-therapy can provide a model whereby professionals with different roles meet the individual or family. This may be at the outset of treatment to clarify the roles of the professionals, or may occur on an ongoing or intermittent basis. Co-therapy illustrates the referrer's respect for the referrers and avoids the views of the professionals becoming split in an unhelpful way. This is particularly important when the referral means that several professionals retain contact with a family: for example, in focusing on lack of compliance with treatment.

A *consultative* approach fits easily within the medical context (McDaniel, Hepworth and Doherty, 1992) and involves identifying a consultee, the person or system seeking consultation; clarifying the referrer's concerns; establishing some agreement on goals and likely duration of the work. As a family therapist, for example, this may focus on the relationship between the family and medical treatment systems.

The context of the work determines the nature and pace of consultations, whether it is outpatient based or part of wider ongoing contact between a medical and psychiatric unit, as in psychosocial liaison work. Questions could include the following.

- Who is making the referral?
- Has there been any change in the position of the referrer within the system?
- Why now?
- What request lies behind the stated request for consultation?
- What is the structure of the unit (the hierarchy, the boundaries and alliances)?
- How flexible is the system?
- At what stage is the organisation in its own development: at the point of expanding or declining?
- How are the facilities available influencing the work, the room, space and equipment?

If we imagine a continuum of involvement of the consultant from outsider to insider, a liaison consultant in an inpatient setting probably acts at the mid-range of the continuum. This provides some freedom of movement, diminishes investment in the political struggles, and allows sufficient continuity to facilitate new ideas being carried forward. However, it means that the termination of a piece of work may be less clearly defined. The outcome of a consultation may have particular implications for the consultants' own position within the system. For example, there may be phases when the outcome influences the likelihood of services being used in the future, as when new links are being forged between teams, or when links are at risk of being severed. Changes to contracting health and social services means that this is as relevant to outpatient work as inpatient work.

Relationships between professionals and families

When a member is critically ill, the *boundary between the family and outside world becomes more permeable*, allowing non-family members, such as doctors and nurses, to enter and adopt roles previously in the domain of mothers, fathers, brothers and sisters. Again, new systems evolve, including the patient and key members of family and professional teams. The redefinitions required when children are ill are tremendous: parents have to accept that others are more able to care for their children than themselves. Parents and staff have to maintain trust in each other, while coping with perceptions of the limitations of care provided by the other. This probably presents a more profound challenge for mothers since despite shifts in attitudes, women remain largely responsible for emotional care in families today.

To ensure the family-professional system is able to function effectively and to avoid de-skilling families, we need to listen to what families have to say. We need to respect their views, their involvement in decisions about referral and treatment, and which aspects of care they feel able and willing to maintain. The interplay between family and professional systems can be extremely complex. We may find ourselves identified with different aspects of family relationships and the situations of particular family members in a process of 'mirroring'. Our actions can become organised primarily as reactions to the family, as is evident when we begin to 'act out' family conflicts between ourselves. For example, relationships between team members can become strained and overly business-like subsequent to a failed kidney transplant. These patterns may relate to difficulties in facing the guilt and responsibility induced, and ambivalence about how to support one another. We can find we identify with specific family members, acting out their despair and disappointment. They may attempt to maintain conflict between members of the treatment team, to avoid bringing despair or anger back into the family.

While all disagreements between staff members do not reflect mirrored conflict, acknowledgement of anger and resolution of conflicts within professional teams may present the family with different styles of dealing with problems and conflict resolution.

Relating to other professional systems

People who are ill relate to a number of systems: schools, employment, religious and friendship networks. When difficulties arise, it can be useful to examine how conversations across boundaries of systems are managed, how differences are negotiated, and whether these difficulties relate to imbalance between systems, from:

- too little sharing of information about the condition or what is required in treatment;
- one group assuming too little responsibility with the expectation that it is being dealt with elsewhere;
- one group assuming too great an involvement with the illness, as when a school overreacts to the illness, becomes overly restrictive or takes too much control;
- each system making incompatible demands on the other.

Where possible, it is important to consult families in communicating with these groupings, to ensure that they remain largely in charge of what is shared. The wide range of professionals involved in patient care can lead to confusion about service provision: professionals can fail to provide care in the belief that tasks are being performed by others, unwittingly adding to the family's burden during both the critical phases and rehabilitation of an illness.

Membership of a specific system may influence the role we can play as 'advocates', when families tell us that the care provided by others is insufficient or unsatisfactory. While any of us can theoretically question the 'care package' provided, questioning the services others provide can be difficult, as it affects the working relationship of wider systems. However, sharing concerns about services and exploring differences in expectations is often an important aspect of our work. Regular network meetings provide a forum in which differences can be raised before they escalate.

Health-care and school systems

Nowhere is this more relevant than when a child returns to school after serious illness in the family. There are likely to be concerns about the academic implications of school absence, as teachers are obliged to fulfil academic targets unless there has been a formal statement of special needs. However, the child, family and school may have other worries: the child may not know how much the class or teacher has been told, who will ask about the illness, or what they will say. They are often afraid they will be asked difficult questions, and will break down and cry. Frequently children isolate themselves or attempt to deny some of what they are facing. Simultaneously, peers will be confronted with the reality that a child, sibling or parent can be seriously ill. Fears of personal contamination and magical thinking about how diseases are caused or cured can affect readiness to engage with the child. Discomfort may manifest in embarrassment, in rejecting and ignoring the child, or in an undue fascination and concentration on the disease.

As discussed later (Chapter 5), while many teachers will have experience with pupils facing a personal illness or illness in a close relative, not all will feel comfortable about talking about it. Few will have had any training to deal with a child or class in these circumstances. Teachers often do not know what the child has been told, and lack of contact between family and professionals may mean that professionals are unsure of how much information to provide to the school. This may limit the child's access to important resources, and can lead to overly protective behaviour on the part of the teacher or even inappropriate academic placement. This can be compounded by families' ambivalence about how the school will deal with the issues, and fears that school may accentuate the child's sense of difference, increasing their isolation. Parents and children should be encouraged to think ahead about what they would like from the school, what it would be helpful for the class to know and how soon they would want their child to fulfil regular academic commitments.

In addition to emotional support, children who are ill themselves may require practical help during the school day, like access to medication or time off for treatment. Recently, some liaison nurses have been appointed to attempt to address the interface between the family, medical and school systems, all of which have slightly different languages, aims and priorities.

Health care and employment

In working with families, we can easily underestimate the extent to which an individual's sense of identity and self-worth relates to their work. Issues about what information can or should be shared with employers and colleagues are extremely complex. A person who is or has been seriously ill may fear that information about their illness will affect promotion and employment opportunities, yet they may require recognition of their needs to 'go slow' during rehabilitation. Again, decisions about information sharing rest with the individual and the family.

Respecting our position in health-care systems: practice guidelines

Role clarity

Families come into contact with many professionals and differing advice when someone is ill. To avoid confusion, we need to recognise our limitations as well as expertise. This means resisting the temptation to provide advice we are not trained to give, and helping families to raise their questions with the appropriate professionals instead. For example, family therapy is not about curing heart disease, cancer, epilepsy or even asthma, but about helping families find new ways of addressing the condition: when asked by a mother about withholding information about the side-effects of her son's medication, my role was to help her to reflect on what this meant, and to consider what medical knowledge she needed to reach an informed decision. She decided to discuss the issues with a medical consultant. Far from a weakness, recognising our limitations is a strength that respects the expertise of colleagues as well as ourselves.

Respect for autonomy

In an age of technological advancement, we need to respect patients' rights, to help people reach informed decisions without imposing the values of the provider system, be this how to tell an ill family member bad news, decisions about stopping treatment, or access to a second opinion. Too often families experience medical treatment as de-skilling. This makes it more difficult to raise dilemmas about treatment, dilemmas which may be difficult for professionals too: often professionals rather than families delay discussions about the resuscitation of patients for whom it would be medically futile. As the family's views may be emotionally laden for us, or at odds with what is available, support from colleagues is essential to ensuring respect for the autonomy of the people we meet.

Confidentiality

While there needs to be feedback between professionals, it is important to clarify what information can or will be shared. This is as relevant in considering what can be shared within families as with colleagues. Joint sessions, writing notes, the telephone, case conferences, ward rounds or informal meetings enable us to communicate with colleagues, circumventing the possibility of splitting between professionals. However, this may not always be possible or appropriate, as too much contact may limit our ability to retain an alternative perspective.

We may have different views on family member's right to withhold information from one another. Failing to reach agreement as a team about such issues means we are less clear what it is safe to say or to ask. With conditions like AIDS that carry a stigma and are sexually transmitted, the ethics of secrecy are more problematic: failing to share information has implications for the health of others.

Responding in emergencies

When working in settings where there is no obvious medical cover (for example, child guidance settings), we need to consider the procedures we will adopt in medical emergencies, such as someone blacking out, having a fit or a heart attack. Although this is always a possibility, the chances of such events are more likely with these families. While clarifying procedures with their medical practioner may be useful, such communication needs to take place with the knowledge and permission of the family.

Conclusions

Treating illness today means that people from different disciplines have to work together in situations of life and death, demanding considerable trust and co-operation. We may have different beliefs about the possible cure and care of the patient, beliefs fostered by our training, personal health, race, gender and experiences with illness or loss. These beliefs influence actions and how we understand our relationships with others.

While relationships with colleagues are influenced by the fit between our various beliefs and expectations, working in a multi-disciplinary context does not mean differences cannot be tolerated: it is unlikely there is one ideal way of relating in an environment defined by illness. Rather, comfortable working relationships are built on a recognition of difference that adds depth to our understanding of interactions. We are inevitably changed by each encounter with colleagues and families: conversations across the boundaries of different systems allows for the possibility of a co-evolution of new ideas and styles of patient care.

Work with illness can confront us with powerful emotions that may affect our interactions with people who are ill, their families, and colleagues. How we manage these interactions cannot be understood in isolation, but needs to be seen as part of a wider process of interaction that includes the systems to which we and the families we meet are connected. This is relevant when thinking of interaction within medical units and interactions between systems, including schools, religious organisations and self-help groups.

Today, where advances in treatment, the push for cost cutting and the threat of closure are but some of the forces for change that professionals have to contend with, systems theory provides a useful analysis of how organisations respond to change. This provides a non-judgemental framework for understanding difference.

Summary

1. Illness confronts professionals with people facing loss, uncertainty and ambiguity in their lives, influencing relationships with families and professionals. Systems theory presents a non-pathologising framework for understanding how relationships influence health care.

2. Core constructs of systems theory include:

    (a) an organisation can be defined as a system in which the sum of the parts is different from the whole;
    (b) change to any one part of the system inevitably affects the rest of the system, so changes in membership of any professional or family system affects the relationship between its members;
    (c) what we observe around us can be understood in different ways;
    (d) an observer is inevitably part of the system being observed;
    (e) there is a connectedness between our beliefs and our behaviour.

3. Systems theory describes how organisations balance the need to maintain stability whilst dealing with change. Medical contexts require flexibility to respond to emergencies and change, yet need to provide staff, patients and families with structure and certainty.

4. Each professional has work where they can act autonomously and where actions are constrained. How any individual operates within a system will be influenced by the fit between that person's beliefs and expectations of their role and those of the system they are part of.

5. When two systems meet, the behaviour of the system that evolves is determined by the fit of the participants.

6. The range of medical and non-medical professionals involved in patient care means that people work together with different levels of responsibility and status. Each professional group is likely to have different expectations of interactions with families, and colleagues.

7. Difficulties can arise when the relationship between the systems involved in health care are out of balance, or where there is lack of clarity about what can be shared across systems.

8. While we are inevitably affected by our encounters with different systems, in a medical context not every participant has equal power in those encounters. Interface between these systems does not depend on negating difference, but relies on a respectful recognition of the value of alternative perspectives.

3

THE IMPACT OF ILLNESS
ON THE FAMILY

The last 20 years have witnessed a marked change in health care: as suggested earlier, paradoxically, improvement to medical treatment has meant an increase in the prevalence of illness in our community. Many who would previously have died are now able to survive and while some conditions have been prevented or cured, for others advances have led to pain control, or a reduction in the severity of symptoms but no cure. So, a sizeable population face living with the uncertainty, constraints and physical discomfort of illness.

A combination of economics and ideology means that many ill people live at home and relatives play a major part in providing their care (Anderson, 1987; Llewelyn, 1989). Government legislation, emphasising care in the community and shorter hospital stays, has had serious practical and emotional consequences: people are released from hospitals far more ill and incapacitated than previously, so caring for an ill person at home requires complex skills and presents a considerable challenge. Even where procedures like keyhole surgery mean patients recover quickly, the move from viewing oneself as desperately ill to being well can be difficult for both individuals and families to negotiate and trust.

Despite this, support for families in our community remains negligible and haphazard. Only recently has the relationship between physical illness and the family been questioned: how families influence the course of illness, and the impact of illness on the psychological well-being of family members. This involves considering how family members define health and sickness; how much attention is given to symptoms; deciding when and whether to seek help; determining adherence to medical treatment; and finding strength to support one another during prolonged periods of crisis.

It also involves considering the demands illness places on each family member, and the constraining impact of treatment. This commitment to understanding what illness means to families will undoubtedly play a central role in determining the well-being of the people we meet in our work.

What is a family?

The term 'family' evokes different images for us all. Traditionally, the family was viewed as the primary social group into which we are born and on whom we depend for nurturance and socialisation. Until recently, this implied a nuclear family in which the father was chief breadwinner and the mother was responsible for the care of the children and home. While this may remain the blueprint portrayed in the media, it is no longer relevant to many of the families we meet, both personally and professionally: there has been an increase in the numbers of women working outside the home, a rise in unemployment, divorce rates are higher and more adults are opting for different styles of cohabitation. This, combined with the introduction of new family forms by immigrant communities, has significantly altered the reality of family life in Britain, a reality we cannot afford to ignore.

For most of us, the term embraces several generations, including our present, past and future relationships. Whether we remain in physical contact with our families or not, these connections continue to influence and constrain us, both internally and externally, as we develop. It is to these relationships we turn for physical and psychological protection when faced with stressful experiences.

We can liken the family to a machine which relies on the action of all its parts for smooth functioning. Alteration to any one part inevitably affects the operation of the machine as a whole. Just like a thermostat, this machine has the capacity to compensate for change, enabling the system to maintain homeostasis or balance. So too, the family is not just an assembly of individuals, but consists of a group exerting a mutual influence on one another.

Like all systems and sub-systems, families have boundaries: external boundaries that separate our family from others, and internal boundaries that create divisions or sub-systems within the family itself. Whilst external boundaries define the character of the family to the outside world, internal boundaries help members define themselves to one another. These may be rigid or fluid, and form the framework for emotional functioning as a family:

where boundaries are more fluid, we are freer to express thoughts and feelings, whilst families with more rigid boundaries discourage attempts to express ideas or feelings which are considered unhelpful.

As systems, families can alter their rules and structure in response to a demand for change, facilitating the growth and development of its members as they pass through the life cycle. Individual changes, as occur with illness, create a ripple effect and mean changes for the whole family. Any problems that develop are inevitably part of an ongoing sequence of interactions between members of that system. This means *mutual causation*: problems both arise from and influence the whole family. Rather than viewing such reactions as functional or not, it is more useful to view them as responses to unusual or catastrophic events for which people have had little preparation. Indeed, where problems arise, like the child of an ill parent truanting from school, they may play an important function in balancing relationships, restoring stability, or even provoking change.

Faced with illness, the family has to adapt to considerable change in roles, structure, and patterns of relating. How these changes are integrated is determined both by beliefs within the family and its organisation. So attempts to initiate change may be addressed at the level of beliefs, or organisation. While beliefs construct our experience of illness, so, too, experiences over time construct what we believe. These beliefs are affected by both past and present experiences: even as adults, the beliefs, attitudes and styles of our family of origin influence how we view our capacity to deal with difficult situations, and thoughts, feelings and decisions about caring for ourselves and others. Undoubtedly our responses are also determined by personal resources, by our physical and emotional energy; our intellect, confidence and threshold for stress; the styles we tend to adopt when challenged, be this assertive, passive, optimistic or pessimistic; and the extent to which our identity and relationship with others is defined in terms of physical strength and attractiveness. Some of us may try to maintain a sense of self untouched by illness, whilst others refocus and reshape personal goals to incorporate or even be subsumed by illness, to a definition of self based on providing or receiving care.

However, individual resources and responses cannot be seen outside the context that determines how we feel about ourselves, the demands of the illness faced, the demands of the health-care system, and past and present family patterns. The way in which physical signals are interpreted depend not only on personal experience but how they are seen by others. How we contain feelings of anger, grief or disappointment influences the reactions of others. In each family, members may vary in attitudes to illness and have different expectations of behaviour. Previous experiences of negotiating physical frailty, loss of confidence or even having requests for help rejected mean that some members may be supportive and others rejecting. These experiences determine the preparedness of ill adults to attend to their own physical needs, or parents' preparedness to recognise a child's frailty. So an important goal of work often focuses on helping family members negotiate and acknowledge such differences.

How are challenges specific to each illness?

Knowing a diagnosis provides us with limited information on what illness means to any of us, so, it is important to establish the nature of the condition's onset, its course, prognosis, and the incapacitation it causes (Rolland, 1987).

For example, the *onset* of a condition may be gradual, as in the usual presentation of multiple sclerosis, or acute. Although re-adjustment, problem-solving and emotional demands have some similarity in both cases, acute conditions require more rapid mobilisation of family resources and intense involvement with professionals. This influences how family members view themselves and how much illness, disability and loss organise relationships with one another.

With some conditions, such as a stroke, there is an initial crisis, requiring enormous readjustment in roles. After this, the situation tends to stabilise. Alternatively, where a condition follows a progressive *course*, families usually experience little relief in demand and are required continually to adapt and change. Where the illness is episodic or relapsing, periods of relative good health enable some family activities and rituals to be maintained, but the possibility of recurrence remains. So transitions between crisis and non-crisis require a readiness to negotiate often uncomfortable changes in role.

So, too, the level of *incapacitation* and *symptom visibility* affects how much people are faced with loss of identity, of intimate relationships and of bodily functioning. With conditions such as Alzheimer's, where in advanced stages one is so changed cognitively and emotionally that the person who was known previously hardly exists, the family cannot grieve as the person remains physically alive (Boss, 1991). However, what is most painful is unique to each family: a mother with multiple sclerosis found it more difficult to bear her daughters' embarrassment and shame at her clumsy and unsteady gait, than what this meant for herself.

Obviously, the *prognosis* of a condition influences the demands families face, how each person finds a way of valuing life in the presence of potential death. But actual family experiences and socio-cultural beliefs affect how we understand what we are told, how much we allow our fears to envelop our lives. Fears of death may take over as much where chances of survival are higher, as with asthma, or where survival rates are poorer, as with certain cancers. Some respond by seeking as much intimacy as possible, while others try to protect one another from the pain of parting, with premature isolation or exclusion of the ill person.

How does treatment organise family life?

Treatment programmes can regulate and restrict relationships be-tween family members and with professionals: having to be watchful of sugar intake inevitably affects parent-child relationships. Such dietary restrictions, medication or procedures like dialysis force families to rethink beliefs about personal responsibility and control; about whether to minimise or accentuate differences, like ensuring everyone eats the ill person's restricted diet and avoids sweets; about personal boundaries, like appropriate physical boundaries when the parent has to adjust an adolescent's catheter near the groin. The physiological consequences of treatment can introduce tremendous confusion, altering how communications can be understood: fatigue, lack of concentration, depression or a look of boredom may not indicate emotions but the side-effects of medication or a limit in the timing of a drug's effectiveness, as with Parkinson's Disease.

Technical advances continually alter the demands treatment places on families. For example, previously renal failure meant regular hospital haemodialysis affecting attendance at school and work. Increased use of ambulatory dialysis at home has eased this, but places responsibility on the family for performing procedures with a high risk of infection. Increased use of transplants presents new challenges. Families may be faced with complex decisions: while a family donor increases the chance of a kidney or bone marrow match, success or failure of the transplant can affect family dynamics. In one family, the so-called 'black sheep' provided a match for his older brother's bone marrow. The transplant did not succeed, and his brother died; what had been an opportunity to 'make good' became a nightmare, accentuating his sense of himself as damaging. Although increased availability of transplants has altered survival rates, adapting to a successful transplant itself is not uncomplicated: there may be shifts in self-image and fantasies that the donor will return to reclaim the organ. Having lived so long with a chronic condition, it can be difficult to trust this new-found health and suspend a preoccupation with illness.

Clearly, changes in treatment affect professionals too: while many find change exciting and stimulating, increased use of technology has altered many professionals' roles, modifying relationships with patients and job satisfaction. Nowhere is this more pronounced and uncomfortable than in facing the ethical dilemmas raised by the capacity of equipment to sustain life beyond the point where it has any meaning.

How do these demands vary over time?

When someone is ill, the meaning of time alters. Dates and ages assume a different level of importance: the illness often changes over time and family members age and move through the life cycle. Both dimensions play an crucial part in determining what the family faces.

Thinking first about illness, conditions move through a series of phases – initial, chronic and terminal – each presenting unique tasks and requiring differing strengths and attitudes from each person. While all conditions do not follow a similar course, patient, family and professional roles shift as conditions progress, so that what appears adaptive at one phase may not be later (Rolland, 1987).

Initially, most people experience unusual or ambiguous sensations but do not know how seriously to take this. Over time, the strength of symptoms mean that the individual and/or family begin to regard these sensations as an illness. Decisions about who in the family to tell are taken. Attention narrows to focus on the body and all physical signals are scrunitised as potential indications of disease. Diagnosis is often the first time professionals and the family meet, so it sets the terms for future collaboration. Usually, one or several family members are given information about a condition. As the shock of diagnosis can render people less able to think clearly, we are beginning to recognise the importance of diagnoses being shared where there is space to absorb the news and return again to ask questions. So too, we are starting to recognise the value of helping people prepare for sharing that information with others, like helping a mother consider how she wants to tell her children, parents and even colleagues of an untimely terminal illness.

In crises, despite considerable panic, families and professionals tend to focus on essential assessment and life support. While professionals are required to provide technical skills, to be comforting and authoritative, tasks for ill and healthy family members differ (Rolland, 1994). The ill person's role may be one of providing information and following orders, learning to deal with the pain, incapacitation and treatment, and forming a workable alliance with the medical team. Other family members need to be flexible and support treatment, while grieving for their changed future and identity. Together or separately, they face finding some meaning for the effect of illness on their lives.

Following this, some conditions enter a chronic phase which may last for years. For many, this requires considerable vigilance and participation in complex medical and rehabilitative regimes. Relating to professionals is often less intense now, so the boundary between family and professionals may be re-established. Family members face such challenges as finding a way of minimising discouragement and despair, and balancing care-giving with personal needs for intimacy and autonomy.

As the inevitability of death becomes apparent, care-giving tends to move from treatment towards maintaining comfort and composure. There may be a change in who is included in family decisions as all prepare for the inevitability of death. As powerful feelings of grief, separation, mourning and loss are evoked, many find solace, inspiration and comfort in spiritual beliefs. Others find themselves beginning to panic, and distance themselves as the realisation of the end nears: this can be extremely difficult for professionals as well as families. Despite the urgency to get things right, there is no one best way of saying good-bye, and what is often most important is accepting differences in what each person can tolerate.

Throughout this, family members move through various stages in their life cycle. The challenges and joys of family life vary as children, parents and grandparents age. Each person has to come to terms with achievements and disappointments in negotiating changes in patterns of connection and separation. The entire three-generational family system tends to move through periods of greater closeness and cohesion, as in early child-rearing, and periods of greater separation, as when children leave the family home (Combrinck-Graham, 1985).

All transitions are characterised by upheaval, rethinking and change. When someone is ill, this can mean that too great or too little emphasis is placed on the illness at the expense of other developmental tasks. Loss of function, shifts in care-taking roles and fears of death refocus families inwards. Where this inward focus does not coincide with the family's natural momentum, shifts in roles and aspirations are particularly difficult: when illness occurs in a parent with young children, the resources to cope with the illness and child-rearing will be particularly stretched. On the other hand, where a very young child becomes ill, illness can prolong the period in which contact outside the family is restricted.

How are uncertainty and predictability balanced in family life?

The uncertainty of illness can leave both adults and children unsure of what they can trust: whether to trust that feelings of tiredness signify having played or worked too hard, or a recurrence of symptoms; whether a toddler's crying and irritability reflects a delay in having her needs met or something more sinister. Indeed, fears of what to trust may continue, with family members remaining watchful well beyond critical periods of the condition. Sometimes, efforts are made to hold on to patterns of functioning that worked in the past to try to minimise the disruption: a family can effectively become 'frozen' (Walker, 1991), responding as they had prior to the illness, providing some predictability in the face of such uncertainty. However, this places unnecessary restrictions on its members as old, trusted patterns can rarely be maintained: the roles of ill mothers, fathers and children have to be redistributed to maintain family functioning. So the family may be struggling to retain a pattern that has limited relevance to their current needs.

It can, however, be difficult to alter ways of responding to illness, even when current strategies are clearly not helpful. When so much energy becomes invested in attempting to minimise disruption and damage, suggestions of alternatives can feel like criticisms, and a statement of failure. Many fear even small adjustments could upset the precarious balance of relationships with catastrophic, life-threatening results. This rigid or frozen quality is often maintained by the relative isolation of coping with illness: few have ongoing access to others facing similar conditions, and feel people unaffected by the condition cannot understand what they face. Moreover, well intentioned attempts of friends to 'normalise' the experience by ignoring the illness only increase isolation and difference.

In seeking to understand how families integrate and control the effects of uncertainty and unpredictability, questions to consider include:

- what action or planning the family uses in facing difficulties (problem-focused coping): whether parents of an ill child tend to seek information and consultation, or reject this; whether they act in a co-ordinated or disorganised way in response to the challenge at hand;
- what efforts family members use to manage or regulate seemingly problematic feelings (emotion-focused coping): whether couples express their feelings directly, or restrain or minimise them; what sensitivity is shown to feelings expressed by others both inside and outside the family;
- the fit between views about the illness across the various family members: children who do not feel their parents appreciate their symptoms may minimise or dramatise how ill they feel;
- how the family view stressful events (appraisal-focused strategies): whether a parent perceive themselves and their families as having control over their lives or as helpless 'victims' (some sense of control seems to allow family members to persevere and retain hope in stressful situations);
- how families balance constraining with enabling one another: how the inevitable restrictions of diabetes to a parent/child relationship and personal freedom is balanced with explaining, acceptance and empathy;
- how emotionally connected family members are to one another: where family members are deeply involved in one another's lives, an illness is likely to have a significant impact on others, whilst less engaged families seem to react far less.

What happens to the family's sense of identity?

The roles we assume in families evolve from repeated encounters in our daily lives and from what is passed down through the generations. These roles are intrinsic to our sense of self, governing interactions both internally and externally. However, these roles may be reshaped and constrained by illness. With a diagnosis of cancer, for example, a father loses his identity as someone who is physically strong, employed and capable of taking care of himself and others, to be redefined as a 'patient'. For both himself and his family, a sense of dissonance can develop between how he is viewed by others, who he 'really' is and was. This affects his personal confidence, competence and how available he can be to others. Changes in shared and private thoughts are equally crucial to family identity. Being defined as a 'cancer family', for example, constructs relationships both inside and outside the family, influencing assumptions such as: the right to prioritising activities unrelated to illness, like school work or family rituals; the right to personal privacy; and what employers or friends can and should expect.

The urgency and crisis so present in illness can add to this redefinition, stripping away layers of competence: families find themselves expected to play a more passive role with respect to their lives, to be the recipients of helpful interventions deemed appropriate by others. Clearly, it is a struggle to find a comfortable balance between the dictates of illness and normative family needs. So easily, family needs can come second to the needs of the illness. For a time, shifts in identity may facilitate adaptation and enhance patient care. However, where this continues for protracted periods or persists after the patient has made some recovery, it becomes restrictive, forcing people to remain stuck in an identity and lifestyle constructed by illness. The emotional, practical and developmental needs of the patient and other family members may be neglected, with a build-up of frustration, stress and poor communication.

Whether we work in physical or psychological aspects of health care, it is essential to help families retain a sense of themselves as parents, couples or siblings defined not only in terms of illness. We need to help families hold on to their competence, and integrate their experience of illness in a way that retains some identity unrelated to illness. As professionals, we may need to re-evaluate the direct advice we give families, considering how and to whom we address information, and examine the language we use to describe ill people and their families.

How does care-giving impact on family organisation?

In most cases, illness alters the organisation of our basic care-giving system, the context in which people receive nurturance, stimulation and age-appropriate limit setting, affecting patterns of alliances and boundaries. In challenging the care each of us expects to give or receive, illness places two (often contradictory) systems of care side by side: one based on developmental needs, and the other on meeting the demands of the illness. For families where children are involved in looking after parents, mothers and fathers need to ensure one system of care does not negate the second: having to help a mother on to a commode or dressing her need not mean she loses her capacity to parent her children, to help with homework, to reprimand or nurture them. At the same time, it is important to recognise rather than ignore the impact this has on the child-parent relationship: that the burden and gratification of giving, and experience of competence, alters the power balance between parent and child. Where these two systems become too imbalanced, the few activities where the parent can still be effective can become a battle ground, like issues of discipline or homework, where good grades can provide the elusive 'proof' of adequate parenting.

Not all members have equal power and voice in the family system: in a society largely geared to the healthy, explanations of illness still focus on blame. While all family members may find their lives affected by the condition, only one person feels unwell, is in pain, and temporarily or permanently dependent on the care of the others. This can affect whether ill people:

- can ask for what they need;
- can complain when they are handled roughly;
- can ask for greater privacy or more intimacy.

Decisions about who to ask for help may be determined by whether requests are likely to be heard, rather than what is age-appropriate: for example, children may have to provide help that particularly challenges parent-child relationships, like attending to personal hygiene, when adult partners are unavailable or unwilling to face those tasks.

At the same time, it can become more difficult for a healthy partner, child or sibling:

- to prioritise their academic, professional or age-appropriate needs;
- to refuse or delay meeting requests in a way that feels respectful;
- to become angry or frustrated with the ill person without fearing they will become more ill.

Although each family will find a unique way of facing these challenges, this may not always feel satisfactory. In working with families, we need to ask how the practicalities of care are managed to ensure changes in family organisation do not block access to constructive parenting, or leave couples emotionally unavailable to one another.

Finally, family organisation is affected by concrete changes in the ill person's personal boundaries as her body is exposed to the scrutiny and intervention of others. The boundary of the symptom may seem to lie outside herself. Family members become attuned to observing and interpreting physical signs, thereby challenging ownership of her body, her emotions and relationship with others. Shifts in personal boundaries can leave people feeling trapped, subsuming all other aspects of family life. Often an alliance arises between the ill person and the person most involved in care-giving, particularly when a child is seriously ill (Walker, 1983). While this enhances patient care, it can upset the balance of relationships, isolating and excluding others. The intensity of such an alliance limits the rest of the family's capacity to value what they give one another, as this does not directly relate to keeping the ill person alive.

Alternatively, when the ill child becomes triangulated, the parents' preoccupation with that child reduces their availability to their other children. Inevitably this affects the siblings' experience of their brother/sister's illness. Fear of affecting the ill person's health means that the frustration and distance created by these organisational shifts are difficult to acknowledge.

At another level, sub-system boundaries may be altered. Having an ill mother may mean that an adolescent child or grandparent becomes incorporated into the parental sub-system to meet the needs of younger children. Past experiences influence how this new 'parental' sub-system functions: for example, what it means to their ill son or daughter when a grandparent provides grandchildren with the nurturance and intimacy so absent in their own childhood. In some situations, the new sub-system may be scapegoated and receives the brunt of the children's anger ('naughty behaviour'). Some of this anger may relate to the curtailment of their usual social activities or confusion about the illness, it may also represent the anger deflected from the unsafe target of unavailable parents. The pain of past hurts may leave residual doubts in the minds of ill parents about the care such a sub-system can provide, leaving them feeling unsupported and rivalrous with one another.

CASE EXAMPLE

A family in which the father had leukaemia was referred as the parents were worried about their 6-year-old son, Tom. He had become tearful and isolated from peers. The leukaemia had resulted in his maternal grandmother becoming more involved with Tom, freeing his mother to spend time with her husband during his treatment. So, in addition to having to adapt to being looked after by his grandmother, the child effectively 'lost' both parents for a time: just when he was struggling with confusing and frightening emotions, his parents were unable, physically and emotionally, to respond to his fears about being abandoned by them.

Tom's mother felt her own mother had been unavailable to her as a child. She therefore felt ambivalent about her mother's relationship with her son. Powerful feelings of remorse, regret and respect were evoked in the grandmother as she watched her daughter managing her relationship with her husband and child under these testing conditions. Engaging the grandmother and mother in conversations about what Tom needed opened the way for them to address their relationship as mother and daughter differently.

Where possible, we need to ensure children retain ongoing contact with parents and have some idea of why they are less available. Preparing families for this normalises the reactions that occur, minimising how de-skilled the new sub-system feels. Discussing expectations can clarify what is required and available. Some families use this as an opportunity to confront past hurts and disappointments in one another, while others find this too danger-ous in the context of illness.

Fears of what changes in roles mean for the ill person may create ambivalence about renegotiating these alliances and roles: taking on new tasks can seem to accentuate the ill person's vulnerability while temporarily or permanently disabled, but still alive.

Whether individually or as a family, understanding others' experience places a different frame on differences. For example, we could ask the healthy partner what she thinks is most devastat-ing for the ill person. If the answer is loss of confidence, we could explore whether she has ever lost confidence. Reflecting on what helps her through this somewhat common experience can promote understanding and acceptance, helping to re-evaluate what is at stake and risk new ways of relating.

How does illness influence family boundaries?

When illness strikes, there tends to be some reorganisation of the family. Transitions occur as the illness and quite unrelated experiences change. Boundaries between family members and the outside world fluctuate, becoming more *permeable* at times of crisis when professionals, extended family and friends are recruited to assist in treatment and crucial family tasks. The support of friends, colleagues, self-help organisations and responses from religious communities run by synagogues, churches and temples can be invaluable. Within the family, one member frequently acts as a *gate keeper*, providing an informal flow of information between the family and outside world. Often, to avoid upsetting the adults, children are expected to manage this informal but essential task.

As the illness progresses, changes in family organisation reflect shifts in relationships with other systems. Analysing this process may actually challenge certain assumptions of family functioning: research with people in end-stage renal failure showed poorer survival rates in more organised, prosperous families with high levels of interdependence than those in more chaotic family circumstances (Reiss, Gonzalez and Kramer, 1986). Understanding this from the family's perspective it would seem that highly organised families are at a disadvantage: having had little experience with loss, disorientation and risk-taking they are less prepared for dealing with the chaotic pattern of illness. So the patient may be excluded to enable the rest of the family to survive and retain control. However, the mechanisms involved in erecting this emotional wall may be mutual: for example, children with cancer tend to distance themselves in order to protect the rest of the family (Bluebond-Langner, 1978).

This shift may also reflect change in the patient's connection with the outside world, with treatment and friendship systems. Realignment and distancing within the family may act as a precursor to the final phase of an illness. While the medical team may provide a substitute 'family' for the patient at this time, to be accepted and valued patients must comply with treatment. So medical compliance may actually indicate resignation and acceptance of exclusion from the family.

How does illness affect family communication?

Illness can have a profound impact on communication, so deciding what is safe to share is one of the most complex issues families face. At the level of information, there are core ethical dilemmas in deciding whether a relative or professional can withhold information from someone who may die. It is probably useful to view effective communication as spontaneous and symbolic verbal and non-verbal behaviour that matches intentions. Research indicates that where communication matches intentions, family members' competence and physical hardiness is enhanced (Blechman and Delamater, 1993). This suggests that exchanging information about personal experience may mitigate stressful situations.

However, open communications may feel difficult when relating to someone whose condition requires onerous attention and imposes suffering on the lives of others. What renders this more complex is that thoughts and feelings change with each encounter: each of us fluctuate in how much we allow ourselves to know and comprehend. Although most family members feel some fear, anger, disappointment, resentment or guilt at times, these feelings may be experienced as unacceptable: voicing them may feel like threatening the whole family. So powerful emotions can indirectly influence family interactions, without being acknowledged: while the illness is not ignored, it is pragmatic rather than emotional issues that tend to be discussed.

Worries about the impact on relationships of disclosing feelings influence decisions about what it is safe to share. For example, some couples find illness alters their expectations of sexual relationships, particularly where there is marked disfigurement or paralysis. Even with psychosexual counselling aimed at exploring alternate ways of pleasing one another, the shock of the condition and change in appearance may leave partners reluctant to recreate or simulate the physical intimacy once enjoyed. This is a painful decision, and one rarely addressed together: fears of acknowledging revulsion, disappointment and grief, or of physically hurting one another may appear protective, but paradoxically can leave partners less unavailable to one another.

Far from protecting one another, these internal boundaries widen the gap they were striving to avoid: just when family members most need one another to create a shared understanding of what is happening, they may be less able to turn to one another. There may be an understandable desire to place a protective filter on how much is shared: parents, in particular, may prefer to wait and assimilate news about their condition before sharing this with children. However, keeping frightening thoughts private over prolonged periods limits the capacity of couples, parents and children to deal with their differences and resolve the problems of everyday living. Often the urgency experienced by the ill person renders them readier to confront the issues others in the family fear.

CASE EXAMPLE

Matt, a man of 56, developed Parkinson's Disease about 10 years previously. He and his wife Pam had a son and a daughter in their twenties who were living in the same town but away from home, and a 17-year-old daughter, Sandy. When referred to a hospital-based child psychiatry team, she had been anorexic for approximately two years. Although Pam expressed reservations about Matt attending sessions, he was encouraged to attend at least once. Subsequent sessions were to planned to maximise the periods during which his medication was most effective, and Matt chose to attend all sessions.

One aspect of the work focused on anorexia directly: the danger of Sandy's position was highlighted, she was weighed regularly and criteria for admission to the inpatient unit were clarified. However, work also focused on what Matt's Parkinson's meant to the family. It appeared that Matt and Pam had always been a relatively isolated couple and, as their extended family lived in Australia, additional support had to come from within the nuclear family.

Initially, the course of the disease had been relatively slow. However, as his condition deteriorated more rapidly, Matt had to give up work, his care-taking needs increased, and he became extremely depressed. Financial constraints and her need for some autonomy led Pam to increase her hours of paid employment. Additional home-help was recruited, but much of the responsibility for caring for Matt was left to Sandy.

While the family often discussed Matt's medication and symptoms, sharing feelings was more difficult. Sandy seemed caught in the middle, aware of her father's needs, yet unwilling to limit her mother's new-found independence. Unacknowledged, these concerns grew. Work focused on encouraging the family to risk talking about what the condition meant to their relationship with one another. They found this very painful, and Pam in particular worried how this might affect Matt. Although he struggled to formulate his words, Matt began to ask her questions that indicated his fear of her feelings, that she might leave him. At one point, Sandy was asked to leave the room to allow the parents to sit together and share their pain, with limited words but eye contact. Reconnecting in this way enabled the couple to re-assess their relationship, and acknowledge their differing needs. Pam asked their older children for more practical assistance, so some of their time as a couple could be separated from care-taking. This required the older siblings to face the reality of their father's illness. Ultimately this enabled their parents to recognise that caring was not only a one-way process, but that Pam still needed the care her husband was able to provide.

Decisions about what to share undoubtedly lie with the family, but failing to ask about certain issues unwittingly implies they are too dangerous to discuss. This needs careful consideration of timing and pacing, and may sometimes mean seeing family members alone first to prepare for what can be shared.

Recognising what may be gained and lost: balancing hope with acceptance

Each family member faces grieving for their own loss while retaining some sense of hope, finding some connection between their past and future lives. Inevitably, we all have different ways of meeting this and may fluctuate from one time to another: some of us prefer to deny what is happening and retain as much pre-illness life style as possible, while others prefer to be prepared for each eventuality; some find hope and sustenance in spirituality, while others focus their energies on self-help healing programmes, like diet or exercise.

In the initial stages, denial may be extremely adaptive, a way of managing confusion and chaos. However, it can be devastating if retained in terminal phases, isolating family members from one another at the very time they are most needed. As ill and healthy members face very different futures, there may be disparities in how they balance this sense of hope with acceptance. As evident above, lack of fit can create difficulties in communication, so essential tasks, like ascertaining the ill person's wishes about future care, can be neglected until too late.

Engaging in conversations about hope and acceptance includes considering practical details of everyday life. At diagnosis or later, this may include discussing:

- how and when the prognosis will be clarified;
- what difference the diagnosis will make to their lives, to family roles, hierarchy and communication;
- who would assist the ill person in the future, if the condition is chronic;
- can this role be flexible;
- what do they most hope they can retain in their lives together.

Often grieving is most intense as the permanence of a situation is accepted. As Rolland (1994) suggests, at these times it may be helpful to explore the following issues: if the condition were to be permanent, what would be most difficult to accept; who would have the easiest or most difficult time in accepting that permanence? As the condition deteriorates other issues become important, such as questions about: the ill person's plans for the future; healthy members' expectations of caring and where members receive personal inspiration and comfort.

Far from a serving as a check list, these questions are intended to act as a trigger to extend thinking about how families balance hope with acceptance. But we cannot consider this without examining our own beliefs, how this fits with the families we meet, and how we deal with the differences that arise.

It would be irresponsible to focus purely on suffering, on the harmful consequences for family life. Illness can provide a chance of experiencing oneself and others in a different way, healing past wounds, offering a new opportunity to experience being cared for, to reassess personal and shared goals. Some families report tremendous self-worth that evolves from caring for one another, learning to value what others can give, developing compassion and delaying personal gratification. Women may find that illness in a partner means they become more responsible for executive action, altering assumptions of what can be known, enabling them to develop a new voice in relation to themselves and others. For men, it may mean experiencing a different level of intimacy, and re-assessing the value of a knowledge based more firmly on relationships, privileging different patterns of relating (see Chapter 7).

These can result in profound re-evaluation of lifestyles: people often begin to live each day as if it were the last, putting preoccupations about the future to rest, while others place greater value on relational intimacy than work. However, while individual gains may have a powerful healing effect on other family members, it can also be experienced as threatening. Engaging in conversations about what has been learned, what new personal or shared understanding has evolved, may enable these gains to be integrated more comfortably in family life.

Conclusions

This chapter has outlined some of the challenges illness presents to family life. The difficulties presented can be immense, placing pressure on the whole family to integrate what illness means to their lives. Focusing on the problems that may emerge can highlight the importance of improving psychosocial care. However, it can inadvertently limit resources by inhibiting our understanding of the strengths and resources with which each family meets its fate. Perhaps this is because much of our research and clinical enquiry remains largely dominated by issues professionals believe are important, rather than the views of the people we are there to help.

Whilst some of the issues families face may be shared, individual, social, cultural and religious differences mean each family responds quite uniquely: there is no 'correct' way of rising to this level of challenge. One family may experience illness as an assault of competence, and another as the chance to re-experience or introduce a new level of intimacy. This means that as professionals, we need to attend to the unique story which each family tells, to differences in how each person describes their experience. It is only in respecting that difference that we can help families face the challenge illness represents to their own lives.

Summary

1. Advances in medical treatment and the introduction of policies focusing on care in the community have increased the number of ill people being cared for by their families. Despite this, support for families is limited.
2. Whether we live with our families or not, they continue to influence and constrain our interactions both internally and externally throughout the course of our lives.
3. The way in which families respond to illness is determined by a range of variables, including personal resources, the specific nature of the illness and treatment, intensity of involvement with professionals and past and present family functioning.
4. Linking physiological processes and relationships with inner experience provides a deeper understanding of how illness impinges on family life.
5. Although socio-cultural and religious factors mean each family responds differently, what families are likely to share is that the challenges they face are likely to vary over time: demands vary as the disease progresses, and developmental needs change as family members age.
6. Some of the dilemmas presented include how to live with uncertainty over prolonged periods; how to maintain an identity that is not totally consumed by illness; and how to negotiate repeated adjustments in roles and expectations.
7. Illness can impose an imbalance in the care-giving system: two systems operate side by side, one organised around developmental issues, the other around the care-giving demands of the condition. Where this results in an imbalance of generational hierarchy, care-giving can limit the availability of parenting.
8. This power imbalance can inhibit the voice of both ill and healthy members of a family.
9. However, receiving care does not preclude giving care to others, both as parents and partners.
10. As the illness progresses, family members face new challenges in balancing acceptance with hope. Intrinsic to this may be recognising what is gained as well as lost.

4

Using Family Therapy Techniques in your Work

Intrinsic to systemic work is the understanding that, as family members are intimately connected, focusing on these connections provides a more useful way of understanding and promoting change than focusing on individuals. While this chapter is not intended to 'teach' family therapy, the issues raised may provide useful pointers for all health professionals. Whether consulting to organisations, working with a family or an individual, systemic work focuses on both the immediate difficulties and the patterns of relationships that may have created and maintained those difficulties. As families and organisations are made up of individuals, work focuses on how individual differences are integrated and managed.

Previous chapters have outlined the impact illness can have on the family, how the practical and emotional needs of everyday life are so often subsumed by illness, leaving parents less able to protect children and themselves from frightening and dehumanising experiences, or portray a sense of competence and coping to their children. This renders it difficult for families to reflect on these experiences, and evolve a coherent story of what is happening to them. While some families feel well able to cope, finding strengths and resources they were previously unaware of, for others the illness poses too great a strain, leading to considerable emotional and interpersonal difficulties. This chapter focuses on work with families where members feel stuck in interacting in a way that feels unhelpful both to themselves and to others.

Research is currently attempting to isolate which factors contribute to psychological resilience in traumatic circumstances, highlighting that:

- what we believe of past experiences is intimately connected to current well-being;
- former patterns of deprivation can be changed by subsequent relationships;
- access to an area of competence, be it at work, academically, in sport or even singing, can act as a buffer, mediating the impact of adverse circumstances, enabling children and adults to establish a sense of self-esteem so central to resilience.

These ideas underpin much of our work with illness. As family therapists, we may work with the whole family, with sub-systems, such as parents or siblings, or with individuals. But, in all situations, the focus is on how beliefs and behaviours are connected to the patterns of relationship within the family: to create any change, relationship patterns are addressed. This is essential as the lack of control imposed by illness can mean families become disconnected from their capacity for solving problems and managing situations.

Establishing the context

As professionals, none of us act in isolation. Our work is influenced by our professional context which defines: the aims and expectations of any contract of therapy; rules we have about confidentiality and information-sharing; timing and attendance at sessions. Although relevant to outpatient settings as well, this section primarily focuses on the context in which much of this work takes place: that is, hospital settings. While this is informed by my work as a family therapist and clinical psychologist, most of the issues raised pertain to all professionals working with illness.

Referral

Before embarking on any referral, it is essential that the referring professionals discuss their expectations of this with the family to gain their support. Where possible, personal introductions alleviate feelings of being 'passed on'. We need to clarify why the referral was made with the medical team, the family and the ill person. Expectations may not always coincide, and care needs to be taken to ensure we know where the boundaries of our work lie. At times, what may be most useful is consultation with the professionals involved. This means, at the outset, establishing how decisions about referral and attendance at sessions were made.

Setting the terms

An informal contract enables the aims, confidentiality, communication and availability of both therapist and medical team to be established. In this context greater emphasis on flexibility tends to be required of therapists in other settings, such as at times of crises, or visiting the ward after an operation. Clarifying what these differences mean is important to ensure there is some shared understanding of the boundaries of the work (for example, whether a psychotherapist is expected to be 'on call' out of hours).

Timing

Appointments need to be fixed at times that will not be unnecessarily disrupted by medical procedures. While meeting families immediately before or after medical consultations seems practical, this can mean our encounters become overly determined by concerns about treatment, results of blood tests or scans, or changes in medication.

Physical location

The physical location of appointments dictates whether there is appropriate space to address emotional issues: ideally, a room is required where people can be seen without interruptions, either on the ward or close by, so it can be used by people who cannot easily walk or who are on drips. If sessions are located in a psychiatry department, it is worth addressing what this means to families as it can be experienced as pathologising.

Inclusion at sessions

It is helpful, at least initially, to see as many members of the family as possible. Thereafter, school commitments, distance from the unit and employment may make this difficult and work may focus on sub-groups, such as, a couple, or a parent and child. Although issues affect the whole family, focusing on such sub-groups at times is useful as they reflect not only practical constraints but the relative isolation of a particular parent and child.

Individual versus family work

There can be no rules for decisions about individual versus family work. Children, adolescents and adults may value the space to reflect on their unique experience of illness. Some may use individual sessions to prepare for what can be shared with others in the family. Practical constraints, requests from family members and therapists' suggestions combine to determine decisions about seeing someone alone. However, even in individual work, focus is placed on the positioning of that person within the family. In combining individual and family work, it is essential to clarify boundaries and rules of confidentiality: at the end of an individual session, it may be useful to explore what can be shared with the family, and consider how this can be addressed. Whilst we would obviously respect decisions about what can be shared, an individual session in which a daughter, for example, speaks of being afraid of her father, inevitably influences the therapist's perspective, indirectly affecting family work. Where there are concerns about violence and child protection, confidentiality cannot of course be maintained.

Your role as a therapist

The role of the therapist is primarily organised around relieving mental suffering and producing healing. This means creating a context in which families can risk talking about what they find difficult and painful and explore alternatives. Although we may sometimes play a psycho-educational role, the main role of the therapist is one of listening to what is shared, and intervening to extend the way in which problematic situations are understood and experienced.

Some therapists see families over fairly brief periods of time, whilst others may begin working intensively (weekly) and then space out sessions at increasing intervals. The intention is that the experiences in the session have a 'ripple effect' on interactions outside a clinical setting.

A clear commitment to listening

The potentially life-threatening nature of illness requires particular respect for families' vulnerability. In a context organised around intervention, we could easily ignore the value of 'being there' (Meyerstein, 1994), of enabling families to use the sessions to express feelings, to share their pain, hopes or fear of abandonment, and reflect on what this means to their everyday lives. An important part of the work is listening to the family's story, how they are incorporating the experience of illness in relating to people both inside and outside the family.

This means listening both to the content of what is being said and the way people tell their stories. Some treat their experience with enormous seriousness, while others prefer to balance the intensity with humour. Focusing on what is said in this way allows us to match the pace of work with what the family seem ready to address. As therapy aims to represent a *co-evolution* of the ideas of both family and therapist, careful listening is an essential component to the work. Listening to the very language used provides clues of how to frame what we say. One father with a serious heart condition used the metaphor of a plant to describe the limit in weight of what his children could bear, so similar plant metaphors were used in considering what he felt the plants now needed for them to grow.

In order to trust someone in this way, families need to experience the therapist as a person with integrity, with a sense of personal coherence (Tomm, 1988). The healing power of listening lies in the relationship created between listener and the person telling the story. Establishing a relationship where families feel they are with someone who is ready, unafraid and unembarrassed to understand what they face – be this fear of death, envy for the health of others, or irritation with comments about their courage – cannot be over-emphasised.

Developing hypotheses

The information we learn from both the process of referral and from each subsequent session allows us to make hypotheses about the family's dilemmas. These provide a framework for guiding our clinical work, a way of acknowledging our beliefs and assumptions, and enable us to test out the applicability of these ideas. This may include considering:

- *why now* someone in the family or professional system has decided to seek consultation;
- *what* people are most concerned about;
- *how* they decided to approach this unit.

Information about *who* made the referral can have a crucial impact on the mandate of therapy: for example, whether the family or group of professionals is most concerned at present. Where the family refer themselves, the primary referrer may be the person who carries most emotional responsibility, usually the mother, or who stands to lose from the current position. This means thinking carefully about introducing issues less directly related to the referral, like marital difficulties.

Asking families questions to facilitate change

Family members make choices about what they divulge to us, so we hear and see only edited aspects of their experience. What people choose to know, recall or understand are similarly edited: we all select aspects of our encounters with others to prove or disprove our understanding of the world around us.

Rather than positioning ourselves as experts, adopting a style of respectful *curiosity* enables us to ask questions and hear how families account for decisions and interactions, and establish an understanding of their world. Together, we can then consider how other aspects of their story can be integrated with their shared and individual accounts.

When families decide to seek consultation, many will have found themselves acting in a way that reduces their capacity to respond flexibly. Asking questions can be a powerful tool of facilitating change: some questions will be asked with the intention of increasing the therapist's understanding, to help us become linked with the family's language and way of seeing things. However, we may ask questions aimed more specifically at extending, reframing or defining the way in which the family view their experience. Being placed somewhat outside enables us to retain a curiosity about aspects of family life they may not have considered. Answering questions framed with a different 'lens' can alter the family's perspective on the issues addressed. Some of these questions will be more exploratory, aimed at how interactions connect people, events and beliefs; others are asked with the intention of being corrective, of planting the seeds of alternative suggestions, and still others are asked with the intention of triggering family members to re-assess the implications of current perceptions or actions so they can consider alternatives (Tomm, 1988). Some useful questions include the following.

Questions about similarity and difference

'In what way are your ideas about your son's school work different/ similar to your partner?'

'How is the way in which your partner treats your son similar to what it was like for him and his dad?'

'Do you agree with what your mother has just said?'

Underlying these questions is the assumption that there can be different ways of understanding experiences, that no one way is more correct than another. Rather than asking yes/no questions about attitudes to schooling or fathering, some similarity or difference may be assumed, introducing a new information and connections, leading to the possibility of risking new ways of relating.

Hypothetical questions

'In what way do you expect your son to take more responsibility for his treatment in two years' time/when he is 16?'

'In what way do you think it will be different for you when your son is older?'

'If his father became more involved with his school work, do you think it would be easier for your son to put himself first?'

'What do you think needs to happen for your daughter to trust that her dad is going to be OK?'

'If you were in your partner's position, how might you want others to respond when you begin to cry?'

Asking hypothetical questions free the family from the reality of the present, enabling alternatives to be considered.

Rating questions

'Who do think would be most surprised/disappointed if . . .'

'who do you think is second most worried that . . .'

Questions like these challenge the assumption that the family behaves as a uniform whole, opening the way to consider how differences can be negotiated.

Triadic questions

'Can you guess what it's like for your two daughters when their brother has to attend the clinic?'

'What do you think holds your daughter back when she disagrees with your wife?'

'That sounds very painful. What do you think your partner would want from you and your son at those times?'

Asking members to 'gossip' in the presence of others enables families to reflect on their experiences in a different way.

Suggestive questions

'Sometimes children find themselves worrying what caused the illness. I wonder if that ever happens to your brother?'

'What advice would you want to give other Mums and Dads about how to treat children when they are ill?'

Your reflections as a therapist

Therapy is not only about asking questions, but includes our own comments and observations of what is happening in the room. In many ways, the process of work can be described as a dance in which both therapist and family continually cue one another about how to proceed. Family members may differ about how much and what to address, and what is experienced as too stressful or dangerous to discuss, so work includes negotiating these differences.

At times therapists *reframe* what the family have said, to bring out aspects of their story that are not acknowledged. For example, the parents of a seriously ill child spoke of feeling failures because they were unable to answer their child's questions about the future. While it was important to hear and recognise their feelings, as important was using their comments to suggest a reframe of the parenting they had been able to provide: despite all, their son had retained the courage to ask, he felt he could look to his parents for insight and support.

Commenting on what others have found helpful or difficult served further to *provide information* and *normalise* aspects of their experiences, comments like: 'I'm not sure if this is true for you, but something other children/parents have found helpful is . . .'.

Pacing of information is crucial in thinking about presenting facts about diagnosis, explaining changes in treatment and therapeutic work. At times, therapists may comment on what has been said to intensify what is shared. For example, where something painful has been said in an understated manner, therapists may comment 'That must be very painful/difficult for you.' Elsewhere, therapists may wish to slow down the process of the work. As always, care needs to be taken to avoid undermining the family's position as experts on their own situation, to ensure that our comments serve not as attacks on, but as supportive for, the family's competence.

Working in teams or alone

We may choose to work alone or as part of a team. This means that the family may have the experience of more than one person observing and listening to their story, opening up the range of ways in which their experience is being heard. Some, but not all, of the outpatient families discussed here were seen by teams including my colleagues, Barbara Dale and Charlotte Burck. Where therapists work in teams, the team/co-worker, often sits behind a one-way screen and reflects on the process of work from time to time, or in a mid-session break. Sometimes both therapists sit with the family. This requires a clear understanding of roles: usually one person carries primary responsibility for interacting with the family. Whether working in teams or alone, taking a break during a session can be invaluable in creating an opportunity to reflect on what is happening in the session, particularly as family interactions can so easily be mirrored in the therapeutic relationship. While team work offers the opportunity of ongoing support, co-workers needs to clarify their expectations of the work.

As we personally are vulnerable to the illnesses faced by the families we meet, access to some form of ongoing support, or team, is important to ensure we avoid 'burn out'. While our own constructions undoubtedly influence the themes we address in therapy, this guards against our own fears overly determining material covered in the sessions. This is crucial as the work of the therapist often necessitates addressing blame and a range of other seemingly unacceptable feelings.

How we use ourselves

There are few clear rules for establishing a comfortable distance between our work and personal lives, or using ourselves in clinical work. Some of us answer questions about ourselves with a comment that a direct answer would be confusing or irrelevant to the family's own struggles. Others choose to disclose more. This does not mean burdening the family with difficulties in our personal lives, but prefacing statements with a comment that reflects our position in relation to what the family faces, such as: 'as a mother myself/being older/as an immigrant too/not being a man myself/as I know very little about your work, can you help me understand . . .'.

Real-life events in our own lives as therapists mean that sessions may need to be cancelled due to illness and bereavement. Although not always appropriate, it can sometimes be useful to address questions arising from cancelled appointments in an open, matter of fact way. It can feel more honest, offering new intensity to the work.

Whatever personal style we adopt, whether we tend to be more or less directive in the process of interaction in the room, our work is not about affecting physical cure but enhancing the capacity to maintain a sense of competence and identity that is not purely defined in terms of illness, damage or death.

The process of therapy

Therapeutic work aims to create a context in which the impact of the illness can be explored in a relatively focused way, where some of the fear, pain and anger aroused can be heard and shared, enabling family members to re-assess how they deal with the dictates of illness. Despite the guidelines below, my sense is that sessions are most useful when what is addressed reflects a shared understanding or co-construction of what the family and therapist feel is important. There can be no set order to the work: families may want to discuss only limited aspects of their 'illness story' at an initial session, and to talk more openly only once greater trust with the therapist has been established. Individual members may also differ in how they want to use the sessions. However, essential aspects to include are:

- clarifying and normalising the illness events;
- helping the family balance the dictates of illness with developmentally appropriate needs;
- recovering the illness as a personal rather than professional event.

In discussing therapy, I shall focus primarily on one family seen in an outpatient setting which has no direct links with medical treatment. Unless specified, here as elsewhere, the family have been disguised to ensure anonymity.

CASE EXAMPLE

Rachel, aged 46 years, contacted a child and family outpatient clinic as she was concerned about how her three children were coping with her disseminating cancer. She was particularly worried about her eldest child, Sandra, who at the age of 15 was carrying considerable responsibility for both her younger siblings and her mother. She alternated between being extremely helpful, and becoming rude and abusive to her mother. The other children were Pete, aged 12, and Lucy, aged 5. Rachel thought the strain was becoming too much for her husband, Andrew, and was afraid of losing him. The whole family were invited to an initial session. Subsequent work involved a combination of family sessions, couple sessions and, at their request, a session with the oldest two children.

Sharing the illness story

This meant listening to how different members understood what had happened to Rachel. The family shared how the condition had evolved, from the time Rachel recognised she was ill, the process of investigation and diagnosis, attitudes to current treatment and medical personnel, and beliefs about the likely cause and cure of the condition. Each member's illness story was different: Lucy (5) drew with intense concentration as the rest of the family spoke but was clearly listening to all that was said. Whilst her mother told us there were times Lucy seemed to be afraid of her, what Lucy herself wanted us to know was that she had a magic mirror. This allowed us to think about whether others in the family too wanted a magic mirror, a mirror that reflected something quite different to what faced them now.

Establishing specific details about events, what was seen and heard, enabled the children to talk about their mixture of fear and embarrassment when their mother collapsed in a public place. Following the pace of the family, I wondered aloud whether the children ever thought about what had made their mother sick, and whether they ever worried if they could catch the illness themselves. This opened the way for the children to raise these questions with their parents, with the understanding that they had permission to ask. Although they had talked about the illness initially, this discussion created a context in which the parents could re-explain the condition, correcting misunderstandings that had arisen.

While familiarity with a condition may alert us to what a family faces, what proved useful was relying on their understanding, placing the family in the role of experts of their own situation. This freed me to remain curious about issues like:

- what they had been told of the likely course and prognosis of the condition;
- what they felt caused the condition, and whether this might be genetically transmitted;
- were they making demands on one another that felt excessive.

While biological aspects of the illness and treatment had a marked effect on their lives, the family rarely discussed what this meant for parenting, communication and intimacy. Rachel was often in considerable physical pain, and felt unsure how much to share without driving her family away. Paradoxically, this increased the isolation between family members: in their different ways, each person was left with private concerns about whether what was being expected of one another was too much or too little, whether Rachel's present state could be attributed to the medication, emotional state and fatigue, or the condition itself.

Discussing biological processes about the impact of medication, or elsewhere of invasive procedures like dialysis or physiotherapy, breaks this silence, introducing into the family's story issues that influence daily living but are rarely discussed. Exploring biological restrictions and constraints on interaction and communication included the impact it had on the couple's sexual relationship and intimacy towards one another. Couple work included attempting to disentangle what the illness meant for their relationship, with Andrew sharing his difficulty in separating what was 'really' Rachel from her treatment and illness. This was essential in enabling the couple to risk thinking about what they wanted from one another now.

The condition's unclear prognosis left all unsure how fast the condition would deteriorate and what sort of a future they could anticipate together. At the end of the first session, each family member was given the task of finding one aspect of their pre-illness lives they could resume, and considering what would have to happen for them to feel comfortable to do so. Elsewhere, where families have found it difficult to make these moves, tasks have been used to challenge illness narratives, like using rituals to celebrate a respite from illness. Even if the family does not carry out the ritual, discussing its possibility can create a shift in how the future is viewed.

Reducing the pace

By the time I met this family, they felt overwhelmed by the illness, as evident in the speed of speech, interruptions and inconsistencies in how the story was told. This may have related to their sense that there would not be enough time to sort things out before they had to say good-bye to one another, and to confusion about how much time I had available. There also seemed to be a difference in the pace that felt right for Rachel and the rest of her family: concerns about her future meant that she was keen to move far quicker than the rest of the family. To reduce the chaos in the room, I tried to slow things down, commenting on my own inability to think so quickly. Clarifying that, despite their urgency, there would be space within the sessions to think carefully about a range of things, enabled us to step back a little and explore how issues less directly related to the illness impacted on family dynamics.

Regrets about the past added to the sense of urgency: there had been considerable difficulty in the couple's earlier relationship with one another, placing pressure on the value of retelling old stories in the hope of creating a different understanding of their relationship before it was too late. However, here as elsewhere, no story is ever complete: therapy involves emphasising that although the past cannot be changed, the process of sharing stories about past events is what enables a different understanding to emerge.

Normalising the impact of illness

Identifying themes common to many families does not mean minimising the trauma they face. Rather, exploring how some of what is experienced in relation to each other arises from the experience of being ill itself creates a less pathologising view of individual reactions. For example, at various stages, it was acknowledged:

- many families find that the overarching importance of illness results in the developmental, practical and emotional needs of other family members being neglected, leading to a build-up of tension that is difficult to address for fear of damaging the ill person;
- how needs and enjoyment of other family members can cease to have a 'voice', both in relation to others and internally;
- how the needs of the ill person unrelated to the illness can be ignored, limiting their world and influencing what can be heard or known still further;
- how expectations of one another can be altered, influencing alliances, rules about hierarchy, and what can be shared with people outside the family. (Here the oldest daughter, Sandra, had to 'be strong' to answer the questions of well-intentioned friends who were afraid of upsetting her parents).

The illness altered their family hierarchy. The parents felt unable to place realistic constraints on Lucy. Linking this to the experience of parents in similar positions, they were asked how their attitudes to discipline had changed, and what this meant for Lucy and her relationship with her older brother and sister. It seems the parents had always had fairly different attitudes to discipline. When Rachel was well she had retained primary responsibility for parenting, so these differences felt manageable. However, this no longer worked for them. Rachel felt unsupported by Andrew and unconfident in her role as a mother. He talked of his ambivalence about how to respond, at times retreating, and at others taking over for fear of relying too much on Rachel.

At one level, the belief that discipline relied on physical strength was challenged directly. When Rachel said her inability to chase her children round the room meant she could not maintain discipline, I challenged this, as in therapy she responded in a verbally authoritative way to both her children and her partner. Exploring how responses were affected by beliefs rather than her disability enabled the parents then to consider how trying to 'make up' for the illness inadvertently robbed them of their sense of expertise.

When a child is ill, a similar process may evolve: fears of firm discipline compounding their discomfort and pain can result in avoiding setting limits, inadvertently undermining parental authority and reducing the child's access to effective parenting.

In addressing the parents' differences in attitudes to parenting, the capacity to retain independent views was recognised. But work also included discussing how, in crises, differences are often accentuated, creating confusion for children who are already struggling to integrate a new experience. Normalising this process enabled the parents to re-assess how they presented their differences.

Although the condition was enduring, fluctuations in its course meant the family had continually to review and revise their strategies. Providing basic information on the connection between illness and psychological functioning helped them reclaim the uniqueness of their reactions, and adopt a different perspective on their situation.

Respecting family's authority

Rachel's cancer altered not only her own sense of control over her body, but the control all family members felt over their lives. Its unpredictable and unrelenting course meant that, as her condition deteriorated, a range of professionals were required to assist in her care, playing a greater role in intimate family life than had been anticipated, helping Rachel dress and bath. Both she and her family felt ambivalent about this: Rachel valued outside assistance, but felt her family could be more helpful; her children thought they could largely manage without outsiders, while Andrew viewed this as invaluable. What rendered this more confusing was that the professionals involved in her care differed in their expectations of what she could manage alone.

Therapy provided a forum for exploring what accepting outside help meant to this family, helping members to consider how they could ensure their integrity was respected. A care worker was included in a session to answer their questions. Meetings like this can be invaluable, particularly where several agencies are involved, or where the care package does not meet current needs.

Integral to ensuring Rachel received appropriate care was exploring how accepting greater assistance could be of value to all family members. This meant questioning what sort of care would feel respectful to herself and to others in the family, for example, asking:

'What do you feel it is important that the people who attend to your Mum/you understand?'
'How do you think it helps that the person who helps your Mum/ you is not a family member?'
'What do you think she most needs from you now?'

Recognising how their ambivalence was making it more difficult for Rachel to attend to her physical needs, enabled family members to recognise how this left everyone less sure of what could be expected of her and themselves, and how it could leave her more tired and less able to perform the tasks she was still capable of.

As professionals, our own attitudes to accepting care may be central in determining the decisions families reach. We need to guard against invading their psychosocial space, particularly where families struggle to reach consensus. This is crucial too when a child is ill, where tasks central to child-rearing are taken over by professionals with their own ideas on diet, sleeping, attitudes to pain relief or the expression of emotion. At these times, it can feel difficult for parents to respect what they can offer their own child. So it is essential we ensure our interventions are experienced as supportive rather than undermining. Well-intentioned intrusions of extended family and friends can also unwittingly undermine families' sense of authority and control.

Reframing illness narratives

As certain patterns of information and beliefs are repeated, they rigidify and become our dominant way of viewing experiences. However, behaviours are not inevitable but subject to change with new information: challenging the certainty of beliefs creates the possibility of new thinking and styles of interacting. Sometimes differences in beliefs can be redefined at one remove: as being right or wrong can have life-threatening implications, exploring how disagreements relate to differences in attitudes creates a less polarised paradigm of thinking (for example, differences according to gender, age, culture or the fact that one person is dependent on the care of the other).

Fuelled by anger, shame and anxiety, narratives of blame seem to be one of the most prevalent and 'toxic' mechanisms we use in facing illness. In their own way, each parent and child in this family feared that they had somehow caused the condition. This delayed and limited their capacity to appraise what Rachel could do, creating a wall between her and her family. It also limited the children's access to arenas unrelated to illness, like peer group activities, which carry the potential of mediating the impact of what they were facing.

Heredity, genetics and hormonal balance do not imply intentional causation: a child's understanding that their pregnancy triggered a mother's multiple sclerosis or that heredity caused a case of cystic fibrosis compounds the cycle of damage, limiting still further parents' availability to children, and their opportunity of being treasured and experienced as valued people. The power of these beliefs cannot be underestimated: denying their reality may be experienced as insulting, as not being understood. It was therefore important to tread carefully and:

- *acknowledge* the sense of blame;
- *interrupt blaming*, by exploring discrepancies in factual information;
- explore the *consequences* of these beliefs for relationships within the family;
- *dramatise* and *highlight* its failure to alter both the illness and the suffering it brings;
- explore the *emptiness* behind the blame.

Less directly, it was useful to focus on:

- what they had all learned about one another through dealing with illness;
- what Rachel felt she had been able to give her husband and children;

- how their experience related to age-appropriate shifts in close-ness;
- how some of their disappointment and anger related to transge-nerational patterns: Rachel had looked after her own mother whom she saw as weak, and had dearly wished to avoid placing her children in a similar position, so altering the 'script' of care-taking challenged her ambivalent loyalty to her family of origin.

Addressing communication difficulties

Attempts at protection impact on communication, leading to mis-understandings, and increasing isolation within the family. While decisions about what could and could not be shared needed to be respected, therapy provided a context in which the implications of these decisions could be considered. As some things might feel too burdensome to say, therapy can be about preparing for the ques-tions that may be raised. Here, establishing what the children understood proved a less controversial starting point as it high-lighted how much was known yet misunderstood.

Obviously we could not talk about communication without addressing underlying emotions, with such questions as:

'I wonder why you decided not to complete your sentence?'
'I noticed you began to laugh as your mum started saying about how difficult it was. I wonder why?'

The actual words we use can easily be perceived as hurtful. Metaphors of illness and death litter the English language: phrases like 'frightened to death', 'I'd rather be seen dead than . . .' and 'I'm sick to death of . . .'. Although they emerge relatively unconsciously in everyday speech, Andrew spoke of his anger at someone using these phrases in an unthoughtful manner. This allowed us to think about what this meant and how constraining it felt to try to be 'correct'. In a later couple session, when Rachel mentioned her obsession with the 'death thing' several times in a flippant and distancing manner, I expressed my confusion and asked Andrew whether he felt this was something Rachel wanted to share with him or not.

While stopping the flow of the sessions repeatedly to comment on communication could be experienced as intrusive or insulting, highlighting mismatch between verbal and non-verbal communica-tion occasionally opened the door to discussing the pain of the illness's imbalancing effect on their lives.

Recognising family resources

Illness altered the family's sense of identity, limiting their capacity to recognise their own resources: faced with the possibility of Rachel's deterioration they had become frozen, protecting themselves from thinking about what was happening. Therapy focused on examining resources both inside and outside the family. Walker (1991) stresses this in work with conditions like AIDS, where stigma limits perceptions about the availability of resources.

Changes in family tasks and roles carry specific meaning for all family members, particularly where they are intrinsic to our identification of ourselves as individuals, family members, and in the wider context of school or work. What proved most difficult for Sandra was the sense that in taking on tasks her mother could no longer perform, she was accentuating her mother's inability, 'replacing' her before she had gone. This required reframing the meaning of these tasks, and considering which aspects of parenting could be retained. Exploring how the parents could place limits on what was expected of Sandra helped define her role as that of older sister, rather than substitute mother. This was reinforced by commenting on the language used: when the father spoke of Rachel and Sandra having some 'woman to woman' conversations, I asked whether he meant 'mother and daughter'.

While change in the parents' roles could free Sandra to engage in more age-appropriate activities, this could only happen if she was convinced her parents could manage with less of her help. Offering a session to the two older siblings on their own both provided a forum to discuss their shared concerns about their mother and a clear marker of Sandra's membership of a sibling rather than the parental sub-system.

Where the condition affects sexual functioning or results in physical disfigurement, redefinition around tasks intrinsic to gendered identity may be more problematic but crucial to address. The children's father having to assume greater care for them did not only mean redistributing roles, but challenged Rachel's sense of her self as a woman with implications for both partners. Asking what this meant for her as a woman resulted in Rachel talking of how her sense of motherhood was bound to her sense of womanhood. This seemed to allow her to risk linking this to their relationship as a couple. She talked of what it meant to her that they were avoiding physical intimacy like a cuddle or kiss. Sharing how they had initially become close highlighted how they were only able to recognise only what was no longer available to them, their shared joy of physical activity and independence. Acknowledging to one another how very painful this was enabled the couple to talk about what else had drawn them to one another, freeing Rachel and Andrew to begin to extend their construction of intimacy and sexuality beyond one of disability.

Resources outside the immediate family were also considered. There were several views about the availability of resources, and strong beliefs about gains and losses in seeking additional help. This led to examining for example, what conversations Rachel may want to have with her estranged sisters to free her children to use the support they could offer. It also meant considering how use of voluntary agencies and contact with the children's school teachers could be increased.

Addressing losses and gains

The illness confronted family members with enormous loss: the loss of spontaneity in planning family outings, of a predictable future and the likelihood of Rachel seeing her children emerge as adults. Powerful emotions were evoked: sadness, anger, guilt, disappointment, separation anxiety and feelings of desperation influenced family interaction at so many levels.

Although these feelings were somewhat different for each person, intrinsic to replanning and re-adjusting was the space in which to grieve. Talking together, hearing and sharing differences provided a supportive rather than isolating framework in which to confront loss and re-assess hopes. The use of rituals that fit with religious and cultural beliefs, and the timely creation of new rituals, can play an important role in facing loss, supporting the care-givers, concretely confirming and consolidating relationships (Imber-Black, 1991). Maintaining precious family rituals, like birthday celebrations, places some limit on the potentially all-embracing extent of loss.

Undoubtedly, the illness awakened previously unresolved loss and trauma. At times the family found themselves paralysed by grief. As therapists we need to recognise how overemphasis on anticipatory grief can become disabling and how much of a 'life saver' humour can be. However, facing loss can also re-awaken questions about the meaning of life, spirituality and religion, providing a different internal peace and allowing disagreements to be healed. Sometimes families attempt to reorganise prematurely without the affected member, or minimise the condition, expecting the ill person to perform functions beyond their capability. As with

Rachel, clarifying the ill person's potential participation is central to enabling family members to face what the condition presents, and find meaning in the loss. Reframing family roles and extending use of outside agencies may increase tolerance for ambiguity, minimising blocks on grieving and the resolution of loss.

Illness is not, however, only about loss. Crucial to therapy is balancing loss with retaining hope. Few of us can tolerate an unrelenting encounter with loss, and need to retain beliefs that maximise our coping and adaptation. Exploring what had been gained or achieved provided a way of limiting the spiral of loss. This included asking what family members had learned about themselves and others; what different activities they had taken on; how this extended their sense of self; and whether they were surprised at their strength and flexibility. This meant considering too what others might think (for example, Andrew's father).

It seemed to have presented Rachel and Andrew with the chance of experiencing themselves in a different way. As a mother, Rachel had valued doing things physically with her family. She needed to find ways of relating and having fun that were less activity-based, like talking, reading together and playing board games. Through this, she discovered new things about her children and herself. Her increased disability also meant that she had to entrust Andrew with greater responsibility for their children, resulting in his developing a different sense of himself as a father. Questioning how sensitivity to one another had changed helped them to face one another with less anger and resentment, and to recognise they had to find a different sort of closeness.

When men are ill, women often have to increase their executive action, altering assumptions of what can be known, and developing a new voice in relation to themselves and others. Recognising such changes may be painful as it highlights the imbalance introduced, but addressing conflicts of interest in this way can free families to respond with greater flexibility.

Previous family functioning

People with cancer, heart disease or multiple sclerosis are as likely as any of us to have experienced trauma and frustration in intimate relationships. Experiences of abuse, neglect and marital disharmony may be altered by illness, but they may equally determine the availability of family members to one another. In the face of illness and possible death, we as therapists are often more ready to notice the courage families show than how the pain of past conflicts influence interactions in the here-and-now. We may, therefore, find ourselves listening to stories of marital disharmony, infidelity, drug abuse and neglect without integrating this into our understanding of their illness story. Alternatively, we may find that such disclosures limit our capacity to recognise that despite the past, current care-giving is experienced as healing.

On hearing there had been considerable difficulties prior to the illness, it was important to explore what they felt they had learned then and how they felt they were trying to do things differently now. As physical illness was the frame of the referral, care was required in addressing painful pre-illness. The risk was, however, that failing to address past incidents of violence could limit the children's opportunity to understand their own anger and violence. Where medical injunctions include avoiding the ill person becoming unduly distressed, this is particularly difficult. Here pacing proved important, pacing that recognised both the stage in the therapeutic relationship and the medical condition. Despite the urgency felt, moving slowly was crucial. What was important was not a completed story but introducing the narrative that anger could be safe enough to discuss.

Contact with medical teams in non-medical settings

Each non-medical unit will have slightly different policies about contact with medical teams. In this situation, the family deliberately sought therapy in a context unrelated to treatment. The unit's policy is to ask families if they object to contact with their medical practitioner. As they had no objections, there was occasional contact with their GP, and the family were informed of any communication. Where families are ambivalent, sending them copies of communications, like letters, may ensure that they feel their privacy is being respected.

Lack of contact can leave us unaware of fairly dramatic illness-related events, limiting our capacity to be useful in crises. It can mean professionals involved in the care of the ill person are unaware of what is available or provided. This unwittingly limits services as assumptions may be made that far surpass what the family are receiving, leading to a process of splitting between the professionals, of devaluing what colleagues are offering. Alternatively, too much contact may mean that we become preoccupied with medical information, and lose sight of family dynamics. Needless to say, where there have been serious concerns about child protection, the family are informed that confidentiality will be broken.

Planning for the future

For inpatients, therapy may not be available in the hospital subsequent to discharge, and discussion of local resources may be important as work nears a close. Where therapy is limited to an early phase of the illness, therapists may wish to clarify their availability to some or all family members in the future.

As Rachel's condition continued to deteriorate, the parents discussed how they could share this with their children, and how to address their growing preoccupation with their father's health. Preparing for the future included ensuring the children knew who would look after them if their parents could not, and telling them who their legal guardian would be.

Where terminal, therapy may include preparing for the future while ill members can still participate. With this family, the television screening of a programme on euthanasia provided the impetus to speaking about Rachel's wishes for the future. Ideally this will enable relationships to be less constrained by what can be said, heard and thought of as her condition progresses. Addressing the future while she can participate may alleviate the likelihood of punishing or restrictive injunctions being issued for the future, so surviving family members are freed to develop new relationships in the knowledge of her acceptance.

This is crucial: medical advances enable life to be prolonged beyond the point where it has meaning, so families need to explore and define their own beliefs about life and death, rather than professionals taking over. They may need to be helped to achieve a better understanding of each other's views in order to reach such a decision. As Montalvo and Elliot (1994) suggest, where family members do not agree on decisions about life support with terminally ill patients, and the wishes of the ill person are not clear, it is important to ensure that they are given the appropriate information on which to base their choice. Sometimes it is difficult to know or agree on what the ill person would want: doing whatever is feasible to ensure their comfort in their last days may be the only guideline available to the survivors.

While the focus has been on relationships, personal space for reflection, a quiet space to grapple with thoughts and feelings about the past, the present and future, may be as important to all family members. At no time is this more crucial than when it becomes apparent that the end is near. For some, solitude is frightening and lonely; for others, it is an essential part of facing what lies ahead. Sensitive therapy can but take cues from the people concerned.

Conclusions

The change demanded by illness presents a considerable challenge to the way in which family members relate to one another, rules about giving and receiving care and what can be shared. While some families negotiate these changes relatively comfortably, others find themselves stuck in frightening and unhelpful patterns. In these situations, families may value the opportunity to examine the impact of illness on their relationships with one another, to reassess how they incorporate illness in their narratives of family life.

This chapter outlined aspects of family therapy which could be helpful to all professionals working with families facing illness. While considerable attention was given to strategies and techniques that appear to be useful, therapy inevitably evolves from a shared understanding of the issues at hand, a shared understanding between professionals and the family. While this does not deny the expertise of the therapist, it emphasises the value of retaining respect for the family's decisions and explanations, the value of a therapeutic relationship in which painful (and possibly unacceptable) thoughts and feelings can be heard.

Summary

1. Work with families facing illness draws on the understanding that access to confirming relationships in the past as well as present, and experiencing competence in some area of life, act as buffers against adversity.

2. At the outset, it is important to establish the terms of the work, the timing, physical location, who will be included at sessions, and reasons for referral.

3. Therapy involves enabling the family to use the sessions to reflect on their experience with illness, without having to defend themselves, emphasising the healing power that resides in a relationship in which people feel heard.

4. This means having to hold at least two dimensions in mind: the dimension of illness, and unresolved family issues that possibly pre-date the illness. While these dimensions do not exist on an either/or basis, we probably find ourselves continually moving between the two in clinical work.

5. Work with families commonly includes:

   (a) sharing the story of the illness;
   (b) reducing the pace;
   (c) normalising the impact of illness;
   (d) respecting the family's authority;
   (e) reframing illness narratives;
   (f) addressing communication issues;
   (g) re-identifying resources;
   (h) addressing loss and gain;
   (i) addressing previous family functioning;
   (j) considering contact with medical teams;
   (k) preparing for the future.

5. Particular respect for family's vulnerability is required so the pace remains measured and co-determined by both therapist and family.

5

WHAT ILLNESS MEANS TO CHILDREN

All children have dreams and hopes. In the safety of a family home, on the streets or in the battle fields of war, children have expectations of a future in which they will grow older, extend their relationships and experiences, and assume new roles. For some, this includes a concrete wish to become like an adult in their world, a doctor, teacher, mother or father. Others fear becoming like adults they know, and are determined to make very different choices in their own lives. Even the most confident children have some concerns about their ability to cope, about relationships with parents, siblings or peers.

All families face balancing the dictates of illness with the practical and emotional developmental needs of their members. Despite this, too frequently what is lost when someone is seriously ill, is the voice of the younger members of these families: the children. In an attempt to redress the balance, clinicians and researchers have begun to document what it means when a child is seriously ill: for the child (Carpenter and Onufrak, 1984; Van Dongen-Melman and Sanders-Woudsra, 1986; Eiser, 1990), the family (Kazak and Nachman, 1991), siblings (Lobato, Faust and Spirito, 1988, Chesler, Allswede and Barbarin, 1991) parents (Barbarin, Hughes and Chester, 1985) and peers (Spirito, DeLawyer and Stark, 1992) with but limited attention to children's experience of parental illness (Roy, 1990, Lewis, Hammond and Woods, 1993). This chapter seeks to highlight the voices of all children confronting illness.

A diagnosis of serious illness in any family member profoundly affects the lives of children, altering hopes, expectations, trust and confidence in those who care for them. Inevitably, as practical and emotional demands alter, so do relationships with family members and peers. Children may have to spend time away from their families, and may be cared for by friends or professionals who do not understand their unique needs, like their fear of the dark and which teddy bear accompanies them to bed. Witnessing physical deterioration or damage in their own bodies (or those of people they rely on) impacts on children's body image, sense of physical well-being, and understanding of illness and death.

Fears may be evoked that children cannot name or label. The uncertainty surrounding illness can leave young boys and girls with frightening thoughts, wishes, feelings of anger, resentment, shame, and fears of personal responsibility. Their drawings and dreams often reflect considerable worry about bodily mutilation. While worries vary depending on who is actually ill, what they share is that an event outside the family's control alters expectations of childhood, of parents' capacity to protect children from trauma. Children learn to observe their parents, to recognise fear and uncertainty, to know when to remain silent, and act out fear, anxiety and anger rather than give it a voice. Unshared, questions go unaddressed, fears grow, and well-intentioned beliefs about protecting one another limit the availability of family relationships as safe and confirming.

Ill children often feel a burden and attempt to hide their pain. Similarly, children whose parents, siblings or grandparents are ill feel under pressure to appear normal, to be seen by parents as able to cope, and by peers as fitting in. As clinicians and researchers, fully recognising their distress may challenge our own belief in childhood as a safe haven, limiting our readiness to recognise pain and confusion. However, it is essential that someone, either a family member or an outsider like a teacher, social worker or nurse, provides the space to reflect on children's verbal and non-verbal messages, and to address the frightening questions they may have. The opportunity to share what is known, to voice their fear, grief and anger, enables children to evolve a coherent story of their experiences, and establish greater control in their lives.

Retaining a developmental perspective

Children's age and life stage influence how families balance individual needs with responding to illness. Their age at diagnosis or referral can inform us of:

- the skills they may have acquired before the illness;
- how long family life was free of anxieties about illness;
- whether the parents had the opportunity to establish confidence in parenting skills prior to the onset of illness.

These factors determine the child's resources and indicate how demanding the situation is likely to be: for young children, what may be most difficult is separation from parents, being cared for by people the child may not necessarily know; for older children and adolescents, the illness may have more influence on academic attainment and social development.

Children's responses also relate to internal development: whether they view the condition as located inside or outside their own body; whether a parent is felt to be separate or a part of the child; and whether the illness is understood as coming from the parent or from the child's bad behaviour (Judd, 1989).

Responses are also influenced by cognitive development: age influences memory, the ability to report symptoms, and under-standing of the cause or implications of illness. Children's compre-hension of death shifts between the ages of 5 and 8 as they develop a concept of death as permanent and irreversible. This alters what sense can be made of physical change, of the body of being swollen, scarred or invaded by foreign objects like shunts and dialysis tubes. Younger children are protected by having less maturity to under-stand what is happening, but are less likely to receive clear information than older siblings (Dhooper, 1983). Rather than ques-tioning who is more or less affected, children probably have different ways of exhibiting distress: young children more com-monly exhibit regressed behaviour or physical symptoms, while older children tend to exhibit aggressiveness, difficulties at school and behavioural problems (Lansdown and Benjamin, 1985).

Older children are expected to perform very different roles from younger children, to act as care-takers and confidants. While this can create opportunities for personal growth, it easily extends beyond what is age-appropriate. Placing development within the framework of family relationships enables us to reflect on how these dimensions connect.

Communicating and sharing information

The term communication refers not only to presenting factual information, but to hearing and reflecting on what is said. Rather than providing blanket reassurance, clinical work provides a safe space in which thoughts and feelings can be shared, allowing children to experience a sense of being understood and heard. They may want to say or hear something only once, but others may need what they have heard or said repeated, to tell over and over how they tried to save their father's life by signalling an ambulance going the wrong way, or to be told they are not to blame for a sister's cancer. This relies both on non-verbal and verbal communication, on joining with aspects of play, yet avoiding overinterpreting or intruding too forcefully into the child's safe space of imagination.

Decisions about what to share with children present complex dilemmas for parents and professionals: how can we protect children from pain and harm, yet equip them to deal with their reality so they can mature with confidence? Children are incredibly good information processors. Shifts in emotional tone in the home are noted: where no information is provided, they evolve their own stories which are probably more frightening than reality. Parents' and children's mutual pretence that neither is worried denies anyone access to expressing or hearing one another's fears: rather than protecting, closed patterns of communication isolate children, raising levels of distress. Anxiety can be reduced rather than increased when children have the knowledge that allows them to anticipate events. Where flexible beliefs about normality and competence can be sustained, decisions about communication produce less tension and can more easily be reached, while recognising age-appropriate needs. Allowing children to reflect on their experience and receive updated information enables coherence and competence to evolve.

How much to tell a child at any one age remains complex. Current practice largely recognises that non-disclosure does not minimise distress, that telling more rather than less acts as a protective device. Where possible, this means providing explanations that fit their cognitive understanding. However, many families continue to share little with younger children (Claflin and Barbarin, 1991). Despite cognitive limitations to their understanding, children are aware of the seriousness of illness from a young age, and given the opportunity, are keen to discuss what they know. Where greater information about the disease is given, there is evidence of less depression in ill children and increased social competence in siblings (Evans et al, 1992).

However, where the condition has a hereditary element or powerful stigma, as with AIDS, there may be particular reticence about sharing information. Discussion with an experienced professional about the pacing of what is shared is crucial, as avoiding telling may have practical considerations for present and future sexual development and practice.

While each child's reaction will be unique, it is worth noting common themes, some of which may or may not be similar for adults (Kubler-Ross, 1983). On diagnosis, many feel numb, attempting to *deny* what is happening. This may prove helpful initially, sometimes enabling the child to attend school and maintain regular activities without unbearable anxiety. However, where this continues for protracted periods, families can feel forced into a conspiracy of silence, inhibiting the opportunity to make sense of their experience. Lacking a story of their lives that incorporates the illness means they are left alone to understand what is happening, giving rise to fears and fantasies far worse than the reality around them.

After diagnosis, a process of *assimilation* begins, as child and family attempt to find out as much as possible about the disease. Children often regress to some extent, reverting to behaviours typical when younger. Returning to a time which felt safer may be an attempt to retain control in a context that appears beyond the control of both the child and the outside world. Gradually, feelings of anger, aggression and depression may be countered by a growing acceptance.

Where conditions are terminal, almost irrespective of being informed by adults, the child develops a growing *awareness* that the illness will not go away, an awareness of impending death. Regardless of whether the child, parent or sibling is the ill person, they may try to bargain with fate, and promise to 'be good' in the hope this will allay the condition. As with adults, it is difficult to maximise the time left without some level of acceptance. However, acceptance depends on the ability of those around them to face their own vulnerability.

In many units, most information is shared at diagnosis. Although some retain almost photographic recall of the event, this is not always the case. Increased anxiety can affect cognitive functioning, so it is important to provide subsequent opportunities to reflect on what was said. When children mature, comprehension develops. As the effect of illness on their lives change, they may need to revisit these conversations.

Labelling and naming externalises a condition, reminding parent and child the ill person is not defined or owned by illness, that someone *has* cancer rather than *is* the cancer. This includes helping children understand that labels like cancer do not mean death, but represent a disease that can be talked about and survived.

Where the condition is terminal, children cannot be protected from the concept of death: sick children as young as 3 or 4 years old proceed from an awareness of: 'I am seriously ill' to 'I am dying' (Lansdown and Benjamin, 1985). All we can do is remove some of the fear of discussing death. As professionals and parents, we need to examine our own feelings about death, ideas about spirituality and an after-life. Only in this way, can we assist children in exploring their thoughts, unburdened by our fears and anxieties.

Recommendations include:

- staying as close to truth as possible, ensuring that children understand they are being treated with respect (Lansdown and Goldman, 1991).
- using jargon-free language to respond to questions and illustrating ideas with drawings helps to explain illness (there are advantages in waiting to respond to children's questions, or until a moment in play provides an opening, but this is not always possible as many fear their questions are too dangerous to ask);
- where possible, timing of what is said should be linked to the child's pace;
- this requires an environment that reduces unnecessary exposure to anxiety-provoking experiences (ideally, discussions should not follow an angry interchange, but occur where there is space to shed tears, be angry or remain silent);
- play, drawings and carefully chosen books provide an invaluable tool for parents, professionals and children to talk about illness, treatment and death; however, young children should not be left to read books about illness alone, as they may struggle to integrate this material, increasing fears;
- communicating understanding in an non-intrusive way may include talking about anxieties, acknowledging feelings of aggression and, where appropriate, beginning anticipatory mourning;
- children need to be repeatedly told and helped to understand they are not to blame for the illness;
- children informing and updating siblings can demystify their experience of illness, allowing them to feel in charge, and ensuring the language used is age-appropriate; however, this should be conducted in an adult's presence, enabling misconceptions to be clarified, and relieving the child of responsibility for siblings' reactions;

- parents are often unsure how much children should know about long-term and side-effects of treatment. Clarifying the likelihood of these effects is the first step to reaching such decisions.

While access to a care-giving network that maintains the child's routine is crucial, on its own it is not enough. We need to establish who is attending to the child's emotional understanding, and to answer the questions so often raised, like:

- How did this happen?
- Is this my fault?
- How was I not able to stop this from happening, to protect myself, my parent, or my sibling?
- Why couldn't they help themselves?
- Why have they done this to hurt me?
- Will it happen to me?
- Does it hurt?
- Will she/he/I die?
- What happens when you die?

Where possible, children benefit from speaking to people they know and trust. But blank replies to questions and fears about hurting others may mean it is preferable to turn to someone outside the immediate family. Differences in attitudes about what can be shared may exist between families and professionals. To safeguard this important working partnership and avoid exacerbating parents and children's lack of control, differences should be negotiated with the utmost respect. This includes listening to concerns about what can be shared, and worries about responding to the distress that may be evoked.

Just as consultation may assist parents in talking with their children, staff may value the space to explore personal dilemmas about sharing emotionally loaded information with children. This can be crucial to ensuring children are free to hear what is being said.

Play and non-verbal communication

We easily err in thinking that if fears and anxieties exist, so too must the words for those fears. Parents often say: 'If only she'd tell me what is wrong.' Children use play and behaviour to tell us what they are too afraid to say or cannot name. They make sense of experiences through solitary and interactive play or non-verbal communication, be this drawing, throwing a ball, or putting toy animals to sleep.

In this way, children make discoveries, try out and repeat actions, gaining greater control over uncertainty and fear. Hitting a 'naughty mummy doll' can express anger against an illness and those power-less to prevent it; it may be a child's way of punishing herself or getting rid of the cancer. Putting toys into neat piles surrounded by fences may be a means of creating order and control over what feels like overwhelming confusion. Noting these reactions is as relevant when seeing a child alone as when seeing the family, where drawings, interruptions like a baby crying, requests for the toilet or reluctance to play or smile are important communications about processes in the room. Where children experience marked distress, play therapy sessions prior to admission to hospital can help children verbalise anger, fear and contain anxiety.

Our comments on a child's play cannot be regarded as a 'true' interpretation of the child's experience, and may not always fit for the child. Rather this work should proceed with care, in a safe context, that respects the child's right to confidentiality.

CASE EXAMPLE

A 5-year-old boy, whose mother had told him little of her breast cancer, drew a picture of a woman within the first few minutes of an initial session. As his mother spoke about his difficult beha-viour, he scratched a deep hole in the place where her left breast was, the very site of her mastectomy. Later, I commented that I had noticed he had made a hole. Rather than making a direct link with his mother, I wondered aloud whether he had any special thoughts about that part of his drawing. This led him to laugh and tell his mother it was her. She said it didn't look much like her, and I asked her what thoughts she guessed he might have. At this point, he asked his mother more directly and she began talking about 'Mummy's sore part' to him.

The effect of her treatment was that she was larger than she had been before. When his mother spoke about feeling tired and unwell, he put his arms around her waist and said 'Look how big I am, I can put my arms around you.' This embrace seemed to indicate his attempts to show both himself and his mother that he could protect her from the ravages of illness and treatment. It could also indicate his wish to protect her from his own dangerous feelings. At this stage, I wondered aloud if he was telling us how much he wanted to look after his mother, and how difficult this was. This led to a discussion of what his mother wanted from him, and what may lie beyond the power of a boy of 5.

Children often sense where is safe to touch or hug. This little boy fluctuated between being careful not to hurt his mother's breast, and attempting to attack it, to destroy the thing that was taking her from him. Therapy may involve commenting on these interactions, like wondering whether the lady in the picture hurts where the hole is. However, the timing and pacing of such suggestions are important, as overinterpreting play can inhibit the child's interactions in the room. Respecting the child's emotional space is crucial to ensuring our interventions do not feel as attacking as the illness.

Working with childhood illness

Serious childhood illness can be devastating for the child, the family and friends. Such children may experience reduced control over their daily routine, have to comply with treatment regimes, and face lack of certainty about whether they will be able to develop into adults who could themselves bear children. Even where treatment is successful, remaining wary of infection for protracted periods can make the world seem hostile and attacking. While some research highlights the long-term psychological difficulties these children experience, others stress that many survivors of long-term serious illness adjust well, and are able to lead fulfilling, relatively anxiety-free lives (for extensive analysis, see Cadman et al., 1987; Eiser, 1993; Kazak and Nachman, 1991).

While research remains ambiguous, children seem to cope best where there is no recurrence of the disease, a short course of treatment, early diagnosis, a family which is supportive and communicates openly, and the presence of a generally optimistic outlook on life prior to illness (Koocher and McDonald, 1992). Hardly surprisingly, these factors correlate with current views on resilience in children across a range of traumatic circumstances (Garmezy and Masten, 1994).

It is, however, meaningless to attempt to resolve these differences: so many factors affect how children come to terms with physical pain, bodily changes, disfigurement, handicapped mobility, medication and residual anxieties about death. The list of what each child has to endure varies according to the course of the illness, the treatment, personal resources and the support available in the family and community. However, it is worth considering some of the difficulties that may be shared. Despite these, however, we need to recognise how many children find a way of balancing the demands of illness with a sense of competence and self-worth that enables them to adapt comfortably, both socially and psychologically.

The loneliness of being ill

Whether in hospital, at home or at school, a child who has been critically ill has to come to terms with living in a world that admires physical health and normality. Illness imposes a change on the way in which a child views herself and is viewed by others: her appearance may be altered, energy levels reduced, daily routines constrained by diet and medication, and fears of contagion and attempts to keep the condition secret can restrict contact with others.

Children quickly learn when their presence is not welcome, what topics are taboo. This can result in isolating themselves with private fears and fantasies, as displayed in the imagery of drawings, stories and poems (Waechter et al., 1987). Sadly, they may experience considerable discrimination: where appearance is significantly altered, concerns about self-concept and body image are exacerbated by the effect disfigurement has on both people they know intimately and strangers. While disfigurement may be slight and not permanent, perceptions of being disfigured and damaged, can last well beyond any manifestation of difference. Reports from self-help organisations attest to the distress evoked by clumsy attempts to deny rather than acknowledge this difference.

Despite policies of equal opportunities, few contexts are structured to deal with chronic illness and disability, adding to children's sense of difference. So it falls to parents and professionals to be vigilant and agitate on their behalf. Although escaping obvious disfigurement undoubtedly renders the condition less noticeable, internalised feelings can influence readiness to engage with others.

Life at school

Although school offers the promise of a 'normal' life, many children still find themselves alone. Hospital admissions and isolation from friends and school over extended periods of time means they spend considerable time in the presence of adults. On remission, children often have to be helped to integrate with their own peer group and to interact in age-appropriate ways. This may involve finding new ways of relating, alternative and less physically demanding areas that can be enjoyed with peers, like music or computer games.

Some conditions and treatment affect intellectual functioning, and require sensitivity in helping the child maximise her potential in a context where she already feels different. This is particularly complex because changes in the condition and treatment mean this effect may not be constant. In addition, many conditions are associated with school absence, and fear and anxiety can affect their capacity for abstract thought. So, when children experiences academic difficulties, we need to clarify where the primary difficulties lie to intervene appropriately.

Living with what illness means to parents

For parents, the most difficult experience to accept and endure is serious illness in a child. But childhood illness is far from uncommon, and parents have to find a way of dealing with their emotions while responding to the needs of their children. Many find they have inner resources they were unaware of: studies highlight the powerful role parental adjustment plays in mediating the effects of an illness (Greenberg and Meadows, 1991). Faced with mourning the loss of a healthy child, and uncertain about their survival or disability, parents can feel overburdened with the care demanded and, regardless of what they have been told, feel responsible for the child's ill health. This can affect their confidence in supporting the child and may result in trying to distance themselves to protect her from their overpowering feelings. A child's illness may re-evoke previous traumas for the parent: in addition to facing the illness, parents maybe struggling to manage feelings that relate to a far earlier phase of their lives. So, this is the context in which the child attempts to make sense of her experience.

When physical exertion could prove harmful to the child, parents and children have to find a compromise between needs for autonomy and protection. Desires to keep children safe can be so powerful that they conflict with age-appropriate autonomy. Restriction can lead to frustration, depression, anger and failing to comply with treatment, while insufficient protection may result in a deterioration of health. Although too much personal control can leave children feeling unprotected, encouraging them to take a moderate role in their care where possible confirms their sense of autonomy. Where the parent's self-worth becomes linked to caring for the child, and the primary form of attachment is around illness, any change can be experienced as loss. Professional consultation may be required to enable parents to allow the child to claim greater autonomy.

CASE EXAMPLE

Alex, a 10-year-old boy in renal failure, was referred while an inpatient. His condition required a strict regime of medication, diet and dialysis. A past incident of failing to alert anyone to the fact that he felt unwell had left his mother watchful and reluctant to trust Alex. He had come to rely on her to tell him that he looked unwell, yet resented that she rather than he 'owned' his body. His mother had invested considerable energy in caring for him and risked losing this 'job' as he became more independent.

Focusing on time allowed us to explore how past experiences, and future hopes and fears affected decisions about current interactions. In exploring the past, we heard details of how Alex's previous attempt to minimise illness had resulted in emergency hospitalisation. Attempts by his father to contain his wife's anxiety met with little success: when ill, he too had ignored his own symptoms as much as possible. Work included returning to the present and exploring hypothetical questions about the future:

- What would have to happen for the parents to feel Alex could deal with such incidents differently?
- How would the parent know there had been a change?
- At what age would that change probably occur?
- What would happen if there were to be no change?
- What did they feel was the greatest risk in change?
- Could the worry be shared between the parents?

While this did not deny how past experiences had affected present beliefs, changing the focus from the past to considering choices for the future altered the parents' own sense of control, allowing them to consider changes for Alex. Having previously stopped listening, it enabled Alex to hear his parents' worries and voice his own fears.

In many units, attempts to increase children's sense of control have led to including self-care skills in treatment, like strategies for managing pain with hypnosis or relaxation; isolating behaviours which could prevent the onset of symptoms; outlining how to intervene once symptoms have begun; and teaching children to reduce exclusion from peers through social skills training. However, high levels of self-control can force children to assume responsibility and develop such internal constraints before they are ready. This can limit their opportunities of feeling safely held by others, of being free to make mistakes without serious concerns about the consequences. We therefore need to ensure that such control recognises children's age and maturity (Fonagy and Moran, 1993).

Exposure to hospitals

Children's experience of illness is undoubtedly influenced by their understanding of hospitals. Some view hospitals as places that make you sick, are boring, or where older relatives go but never returned. While some television programmes and books portray hospitals as places of healing and safety, this will be ineffective if disqualified by personal experience. Work by Bowlby and Robertson (1952), highlighting the devastating impact of insensitively handled separations of young children from parents, has resulted in national guidelines for shortening hospital stays where possible. Attempts have also been made to minimise the number of professionals each child comes into contact with while in hospital, and where possible children have a designated keyworker. The Department of Health has also legislated for educational provision during admissions, with suggestions of provision for siblings on paediatric wards (Department of Health, 1991).

Although financial constraints mean that this is not always available, a hospital-based school can serve as a forum for children to keep up with their work, engage in age-appropriate activities and, most importantly during long admissions, relate to peers. As such, it provides an informal support group and source of information, including, for example, current success rates of transplants. This means that when a child who had a transplant is readmitted to the unit in renal failure, news is quickly relayed to others on the ward.

In some cases, parents' realisation of children's physical frailty can lead to pressure being put on academic performance. While the diversion of schooling may be a welcome relief for some, many children are too ill to concentrate, so attempts to normalise their experience through simulating the school experience have to be handled carefully.

The role of gender in determining vulnerability

Finally, there are suggestions that gender influences children's experience of illness. Research suggests that boys are physically more vulnerable than girls. This has been largely linked with differences in the immune system (Gualtieri and Hicks, 1985). But there are also suggestions that boys show greater emotional and behavioural difficulties associated with disease (Hurtig and White, 1986; Sanger, Copeland and Davidson, 1991). This raises questions of whether our expectations of responding to illness, the emotional expression and behaviour seen as appropriate in hospital, at school, or at home is different for boys and girls. For example, there are suggestions that regardless of the severity of sickle-cell anaemia, mothers see sons as sicker than daughters and are more restrictive of boys' activities (S. A. Hill and Zimmerman, 1995). It is difficult to know how general this is, but clinically it is worth examining whether our expectations are based on what is age-appropriate or gender-appropriate, and whether this aids or inhibits the flexibility of both child and family.

Working with children who have an ill sibling

The physical and emotional needs of ill children means that all too often families and professionals become preoccupied with that child, ignoring their siblings during what may be a frightening and confusing period. Many become caught in a *double bind*, attempting to 'make up' for the ill sibling, to fill the gap and succeed in areas no longer available to them. Supplanting oneself in those very areas can feel dangerous, highlighting what the other can no longer achieve. It can become more problematic to express rivalry, to test the limits of their abilities and enjoy their strengths and achievements. Distress may be disguised by the importance of appearing to be coping well, leaving the family free to focus on the ill child. Minimising how illness affects their own lives means that while siblings give a public account of coping, they may have quite different private thoughts, thoughts dominated by personal responsibility, guilt, fears of developing the condition, feelings of neglect and resentment about being burdened by extra domestic chores. These thoughts can remain unexpressed but continue to affect decisions later as adults.

All children deal with these dilemmas differently (see reviews by Lobato, Faust and Spirito, 1988; Evans *et al.*, 1992; Engstrom, 1992). Certain studies suggest they show little differences in rates of disturbance compared with siblings of healthy children. Elsewhere, researchers and clinicians argue that the burden placed on these children can be enormous, resulting in social withdrawal, aggression, poor peer relationships, low self-esteem, anxiety, jealousy, academic underachievement and enuresis. For many, their anxiety and low self esteem seem to mirror and even surpass the feelings of their ill siblings.

The picture is not one-sided: illness can provide a growth experience through which children develop compassion, sensitivity and understanding. However, crucial in determining this capacity to cope is access to a source of personal recognition, to an area of personal competence and knowledge, enabling the child to retain self-worth and mediate the guilt induced by being healthy.

The practical demands siblings face may vary, depending on gender: in certain cultural groups, sisters of ill and handicapped siblings carry greater responsibility for household tasks and care of other siblings than brothers (Eiser, 1990). Paradoxically, although such responsibility restricts sisters' freedom, it provides a sense of connectedness, control and agency in the face of unpredictability. Although a sibling's illness may evoke increased needs for intimacy in all children, this response may be less available to boys: their relative freedom means they can pursue activities outside the home, like sport, but this may increase their isolation.

Undoubtedly witnessing illness constructs children's understanding of what sibling relationships mean, the rules they evolve of how to negotiate rivalry, envy and guilt as brothers and sisters; whether personal achievements can be recognised in the face of others' suffering; and the right to own a voice that expresses their own rather than another's needs.

Parents' own response to the illness and the support they too receive impacts on their readiness to recognise distress in healthy children. As importantly, sibling relationships in their own family of origin inevitably construct beliefs and hopes of these relationships, influencing how rivalrous situations are mediated, and whether difference can be tolerated or accepted. Clinically, it is useful to explore:

- where siblings receive support in times of crisis;
- how the constraints of illness are balanced with fun in family life;
- whether children are allowed to express rivalry;
- how parents provide some protection against feelings that could seem overwhelming, so siblings can relate to one another unburdened by fears of being destructive.

Recognising and normalising fears reassures children that feelings are not of themselves harmful: they cannot cause illness or kill. In some situations, a family consultation may prove useful.

CASE EXAMPLE

Returning to Alex, prior to diagnosis he had been extremely able, both academically and at sport. His comments on the ward indicated acute feelings of guilt and powerlessness about what his illness meant for his twin brother, Jack. He and his parents dealt with this by trying to limit the seriousness of his illness in Jack's presence. This meant Jack was left unsure whether he could trust what was shared with him. Unlike his brother, he struggled academically, was extremely accident-prone, and preoccupied with his own health.

A family consultation enabled us to consider Jack's understanding of the illness, to clarify and demystify what was happening around him. This meant addressing his fears that he was to blame for his brother's deterioration, when an adverse change occurred after an argument. Alex said he was relieved it was he rather than Jack who was ill. His parents were horrified by this statement, but it allowed Jack to share how hard it was to try to make up for his brother.

Introducing questions that focused on one member's relationships with another, such as asking one member to comment on the relationship between two others (triadic questions), introduced a sense of difference into the room. Asking the parents whether they felt Jack would ever succeed at rugby like his brother focused attention on a second covert message: replacing Alex's achievements was as burdensome as living up to expectations, as this emphasised what his brother could no longer do. This allowed the brothers to acknowledge their difference and separateness, enabling some of their anger towards the illness and one another to be faced. The fact that they were of the same gender probably influenced how much they were compared to one another, both within the family and by others.

Asking hypothetical questions, like what he would do if magically, Alex was well, enabled Jack's own voice to be heard, focusing on his capabilities and interests rather than deficits. As his interests were different to his brother's (that is, music), this was less challenging to positions in the family. In this way, the brothers were able to capitalise on what they could give one another without denying their real differences.

Both at diagnosis and as the condition progresses, clear information, reassurance and support help children develop a coherent understanding of their own experience. Unless the ages are very different, it is preferable to avoid giving them more information than their ill sibling. In all our contexts, we need to introduce questions about siblings, ask who is attending to their requirements, be available to answer their questions and maintain regular routines. Leaflets and story books can help raise their profile in the minds of families and professionals. Some units have introduced group discussions for siblings, with or without the rest of family. These include psycho-educational components, aimed at normalising feelings, and a space for siblings to listen to one another's stories (Gonzalez, Steinglass and Reiss, 1989). As these relationships are precursors to psychological well-being in later life, our self-esteem, trust in others and capacity to negotiate difference, it is essential they receive greater attention.

Working with children who have an ill parent

While children do learn from what they are told directly, they learn too from observing the non-verbal reactions of people they encounter intimately. Witnessing a parent in pain, struggling with fatigue, nausea and discomfort can have a profound impact on how they make sense of their lives, influencing hopes and expectations for the future. Children have to find a way of balancing this awareness with their own needs, with school work and play, influencing their responses to others, inside and outside the family.

To date, little research has focused on this area: it is as if it is too difficult for us to fully comprehend what it is like for children to watch a parent in pain, visit an adult ward, or to feel angry with a mother who can no longer run or talk. Few adult wards or hospices have space set aside for the children of ill patients to play, adding to the alienating experience of the setting for both children and parents.

Again, the research we do have (see Roy, 1990, and Parker, 1993, for fuller discussion) seems to suggest that while some children are able to maintain a relationship with their parents that allows them to engage in age-appropriate activities, others find this more difficult: approximately one-third of children struggle to adjust to chronic parental illness, with many displaying considerable aggression, anxiety, sadness, sibling rivalry and fear of separation; they have restricted social activities and are ashamed to tell peers their parent is ill or disabled. Others still become preoccupied with their body, with some conditions (like maternal breast cancer) often arousing specific psychosexual anxieties (Wellisch *et al.*, 1992).

However, parental illness is not only about children's suffering: many gain from this experience, from the intimacy evoked between family members, and the development of competence that comes from assuming greater responsibility. We still know little of what protects children at risk in this way, but we do know that their experience is influenced by the extent of disruption to their lives. They seem to fare better where they can continue to be cared for by the person they regard as their primary care-giver, and currently this means when a father rather than a mother is ill. Interestingly, a similar picture emerges with disability, with fewer entering local authority care when fathers rather than mothers are affected. This highlights the importance of helping families maintain continuity of care where possible.

Children's anxiety is influenced by how parents manage their own anxiety (Rosenheim and Reicher, 1986). The healthy parent's response to a partner's illness, such as being unable to contain feelings of anger and depression, can mean that children effectively lose not one but both parents during crises. Parents' guilt about the practical and financial restrictions imposed by illness may also remain with them for years, with regrets influencing family life well beyond the duration of illness.

Although children may recognise differences in the opportunities they and their peers have, how these differences are understood and experienced seems to determine their responses. Despite the many contradictions they face, the capacity to know and value their own understanding is crucial to evolving a story of the illness that fits with their personal experience. This means listening to children's stories, encouraging them to find and express their own voice and private longings. Like all children whose parents have been victims of trauma, many experience guilt and ambivalence about their right and freedom to live the active life unavailable to their parents. Although we all have to negotiate this as our parents age, when it occurs in the life of a young child or adolescent, their needs for care-taking, connection and independence render this more problematic.

Central, too, are the actual expectations they and others have: whether they have the cognitive and physical capacity, and permission, to fulfil those expectations. Expectations may be at the level of domestic chores, or may include assuming emotional responsibility for the well-being of their parents and themselves. Many find themselves caught in a complex double bind of how much to do or give: ill parents may need the sort of assistance their adult partners are unwilling or unable to provide. While stepping in to help lets the other parent off the hook, the child's actions highlight their parent's refusal and limitations.

These issues are further complicated by how ill parents themselves manage their own reduced capacities and pain. Focusing on age enables us to explore what these triangles mean: how decisions about expectations of children and their ill parents are reached: whether a distinction is drawn between *parenting*, the emotional responsibility parents have for children, and *parental activities*, the things people do as parents (Parker, 1993). While barriers to practical aspects of child care are inevitable for many ill parents, this is less true of emotional availability: it is this availability that contributes most powerfully to the child's well-being. Undertaking some parental activities may be manageable for a child, leading to an enhanced sense of self-esteem, but being required to fulfil wider responsibility in the absence of receiving this support themselves is particularly burdensome. Recognising this difference can help parents remain emotionally available to children for longer, avoiding pushing them into premature independence.

There are times when parents can no longer retain this responsibility, either temporarily or permanently. Almost inevitably, these children have to face responsibilities earlier than might otherwise have been expected, possibly more so where their parent does not have a partner. We need, therefore, to explore the availability of other adults within and outside the family. To do so means initially establishing whether the ill parent can focus on issues like how the child is managing school life, and then exploring who could be recruited to help. But it also involves ensuring children are not solely responsible for their parent's welfare, including decisions about introducing respite or hospice care.

Caring for ill and disabled parents places children in a predominantly adult-defined context. This can be true too when the condition is kept secret. Children have an uncanny ability to sense any danger or threat of loss. When questions are met with unqualified reassurance or reactions inhibit further discussion, fantasies of responsibility and anxiety grow. Although home treatment and visible symptoms may make sharing information unavoidable, many choose not to tell children anything until the anxiety has lifted.

CASE EXAMPLE

Tanya, a 8-year-old only child of academic parents, was referred to the clinic with learning problems. This had begun about three years previously, as had difficulties relating to peers and a reluctance to spend time away from home. An intellectual assessment indicated that her academic performance was well below what could be expected of her. In family discussions, she complained bitterly of her father's smoking, but questions about why she was worried about his health met with a blank response.

What became apparent was how watchful she was of her parents. I commented on what a good listener Tanya was, what an important job that might be in the family. At this point, her parents requested a consultation on their own, during which they revealed that Tanya's mother had been treated for thyroid cancer about two years previously. Despite Tanya having attended an out-patient appointment with her mother when childminding made this inevitable, they felt she was unaware of the cancer. We began to explore how injunctions against making sense of what she saw could affect Tanya's current learning. This meant asking the parents:

- what they feared she might think;
- whether she might be worried about her mother's health;
- what would happen if she learned now of her mother's earlier illness.

The couple discussed how they had reached their previous decision and were asked to consider what was different now. At the time of diagnosis, Tanya's mother felt it would be destructive for her to learn she was ill, as if she asked anyone about cancer she may be told her mother would die. Although he disagreed with his partner, the father did not intervene as it was her illness they were discussing, rather than his own.

Their own beliefs and fears about cancer influenced what they could share with Tanya. Work involved helping the parents confront fears about their own vulnerability, and acknowledge their different voices as parents. It also meant considering how they could talk to Tanya, to help her understand they were taking sufficient care of their own health. That evening, at home and in their own way, they told their daughter of her mother's earlier illness. They decided to avoid the using the word cancer until they felt she could deal with the responses this might evoke in others.

It is often useful to ask whether children:

- have information they can understand about their parent's condition;
- know what to do in crises, including first aid procedures and access to an emergency telephone number;
- have access to someone they can trust with questions and fears;
- know about plans for their future.

It also important to establish whether household and care-giving tasks are distributed on a realistic basis, according to age and availability, not gender, and whether daily routines are maintained as far as possible. We need to begin to consider provisions for children in adult-centred units too, and explore how parents can help children balance their own requirements with their parents' increased demands for practical assistance.

Where an extended family member is ill

Approximately 86 per cent of us are likely to have chronic health problems in later life (Zarit, Todd and Zarit, 1986). Frequently, this means going to live with an adult child or sibling when ill, or relying on the support of a daughter or daughter-in-law while in hospital or hospice care. Reversing the balance of care-taking like this can seriously affect an elderly person's sense of dignity, requiring subtle negotiation of roles. This is particularly difficult where the condition involves communication disorders and personality changes, or where painful issues have been left unresolved for years.

Adult children, often parents themselves, report difficulties in matching these demands with those of child-rearing, feeling nothing they can do is enough. Indeed, research details the detrimental effect this can have on their own physical and emotional well-being (Kriegsman, Penninx and van Eijk, 1995). However, young children too have much to gain from interacting with extended family members in this way, extending their sense of compassion and sensitivity as they watch their parents care for others, and accepting ageing and illness as intrinsic to the human condition.

However, they still need to experience a sense of being looked after, to have access to their own parents or trusted adults to ensure they do not feel neglected or become preoccupied with health. In helping families plan care packages, we would do well to consider how these demands conflict and provide space for families to plan for what this may mean to their lives.

The particular needs of adolescents

Improved treatment means more children survive and reach adolescence with scars of pre-natal abnormalities, face puberty while on life-sustaining equipment, and enter adulthood with conditions that used to be fatal in childhood. More face the possibility of having a parent or sibling who is not well, either currently or in the past, and concerns about whether they and their family will survive.

Certain issues are accentuated in adolescence: while this is the stage most girls and boys renegotiate their connection to and independence of parents, illness inhibits freedom to extend relationships outside the family. Facing experiences that have not confronted peers can introduce an added sense of difference, affecting self-confidence. Recognising this is crucial to helping adolescents find ways of relating that do not accentuate this.

Physical appearance
Although important at all ages, for adolescents, preoccupations with physical appearance are at their height. Treatment can involve transplants, surgery, inserting catheters, shunts or tubes, possibly resulting in scarring. Medication may be required that bloats the body, as may cumbersome aids like wheelchairs. Integral to what physical change and disfigurement mean are concerns about peer reactions. Not only an ill person, but teenage brothers, sisters, daughters and sons may be embarrassed about their disfigured appearance, fear becoming like them, or feel guilty about being physically attractive and less damaged. Indeed, an adolescent's embarrassment about another's appearance can be so powerful it affects the ill person's response, resulting in their avoiding the use of aids that would make them more independent, like a zimmer frame.

Paradoxically, denying difference can heighten anxiety, suggesting that disfigurement is so shameful it cannot be acknowledged. Recognising these fears is essential to helping adolescents accept the damaged part of themselves, their parents or their siblings.

Control and care-taking
Becoming care-givers of parents or siblings invests adolescents with enormous control and responsibility. As professionals, we too have

an investment in recognising their courage and capability as care-givers. Limited resources can mean that we inadvertently encourage adolescents to give up their rights to be looked after, making it more difficult for resentments to be voiced, for feelings of wanting a life unconstrained by illness to be heard. For many, school work assumes a low priority; for others, peer relationships become restricted by limited expectations of a life beyond care-taking. Although we may not have a rigid view of how families should be, firmly retaining a developmental perspective can enable us to assess expectations, and to question who would know when resources are being stretched too far. Conversations with someone outside the family enables alternatives to be explored, reconnecting adolescents with the right to voice age-appropriate needs.

CASE EXAMPLE

This was particularly evident in a lone-parent family, where the mother suffered from a deteriorating condition, multiple sclerosis. Although her adolescent son's and daughter's expectations of what they could provide were high, they found themselves becoming increasingly angry with their mother. The younger son (12) spent more time outside the home. While the daughter (15) resented the limitations caring placed on her life, she feared the world outside the dictates of illness, remaining locked into a pattern that felt uncomfortable to all.

The balance of power imposed by caring for their mother meant that although they had to carry out complex tasks of caring for her, there was little opportunity for real feedback on how successfully these tasks were managed. Whilst the mother experienced the care as rough and insufficiently thorough, she was unable to tell them.

Only when difficulties escalated was the extent to which they were having to engage in caring for their mother recognised. Ambivalence about their roles meant that they found it difficult to hear what outside agents could offer their mother. Work with this family included exploring resources in the extended family. It also involved inviting professionals in her wider care network to a session to enable the family to ask questions about multiple sclerosis and consider how respite care could be integrated into their lives. The family were curious about how many carers might be involved, how privacy could be preserved and what other families wanted. Although the adolescents' reticence may have reflected their mother's ambivalence, it was only after practical issues had been considered that they were able to hear what their mother wanted.

Compliance

Some conditions, like diabetes and kidney failure, require a medical regime with specific dietary, sleep, alcohol and drug restrictions. At adolescence, peers are most likely to test their physical limits and experiment with alternative lifestyles. As this is less available to the ill adolescent, experimentation can prove problematic for siblings too.

For someone whose life is severely restricted by illness, refusing to comply with treatment may mean several things: it may be a forum of rebellion, attacking and challenging parents for the unrelenting dependence of illness; an attempt to prove physical strength; or a statement about a commitment to a life free from illness. Sadly, the cost of rebellion can be enormous, resulting in restricted growth, delayed puberty and a generalised hastening of the disease process with kidney failure, and coma or premature death with diabetes. Paradoxically, despite apparent lack of control, this costliness places adolescents in positions of enormous control, locking children and parents into interactions that are helpful to neither, but retained for fear that anything new might worsen things. Professionals need to help families separate issues of independence, rebellion and control from treatment. Reframing this behaviour as a process that engages all adolescents, the struggle to achieve separation yet remaining connected to families, provides an alternative and less frightening construction of events. This normative framework enables families to recognise their own expertise and experience of adolescence, and explore other avenues of self-assertion (Altschuler *et al.*, 1991).

Schools: an underutilised resource

Until recently, schools have been relatively underutilised in helping children confront illness. Those whose absence was at the start of schooling seem to struggle most, with maths frequently being quoted as presenting particular problems in secondary school. Sadly, teasing remains a common occurrence. Recent initiatives have led to greater liaison between hospitals and schools, presentations by medical staff at school and counselling as a means of assisting a child reintegrate after serious illness. Most school-based interventions consider ill children, rather than children with ill parents or siblings. They also tend to provide factual information with less emphasis on helping children integrate their own thoughts and feelings (Charlton, Pearson and Morris-Jones, 1986). Bearing in mind how many in our community become seriously ill, every teacher will have known a child who faced illness in someone close to them whilst at school. Some will have chosen to acknowledge this to the child or class, while others will not. Clearly, addressing what illness means in the classroom setting requires a serious commitment from staff members, including support from senior levels of management too. Teachers may have personal anxieties about exposure to illness, and professional dilemmas about managing the academic consequences of distress for the rest of the class. There may be concerns about raising anxieties in children as yet unaffected by illness or loss. However, clinically, teachers' comments indicate they are keen for advice in these situations; for many children, school is the one safe place they can bring their innermost fears: their drawings and essays are filled with images and stories that reflect a tremendous preoccupation with death and illness. Where available, school counsellors or special needs teachers can act as a support, working with whole classes or individual children:

- liaising between medical team, parents and school;
- exploring resources such as books, videos and arranging visits from medical personnel;
- clarifying misconceptions, enabling the class to act more supportively;
- helping the child gain a clearer understanding of the illness;
- if appropriate, exploring whether the child can be entrusted with manageable caring tasks to create a greater sense of control at home;
- normalising and facilitating acceptance of the powerful emotions aroused;
- helping organise time, balancing academic commitments with the constraints of family responsibilities;
- exploring ways of maintaining contact with class and homework during periods of hospitalisation;
- exploring opportunities of experiencing choice in the school day, like selecting activities or schedules;
- encouraging ill children to engage in extracurricular and social activities, and, where necessary, assisting families to seek funding or special arrangements for transport.

When additional classroom assistance is provided, very young children may be reluctant to become involved with another professional, particularly if the teacher has had personal contact with an ill parent. Rather than a new person dealing with the child, they may teach the class while the teacher is freed to respond more directly to the child. However, there are times when having to act as a substitute for an ill parent is so stressful that it is a healthy relief for the support teacher to work with the child.

Working with a child facing so much suffering can rob teachers, like all professionals, of their sense of competence. Creating some forum to reflect on experience can allow discussions to evolve: about containing emotions in the class, and dealing with acting out behaviour or bullying; to reconnect with the value of providing firm boundaries a child can test and trust; to explore how to balance this with responding flexibly to distress in the classroom. Teachers may value discussing their response to emotionally charged comments, to essays about a mummy dying or a child never being looked after, and how to indicate understanding without putting words and thoughts into children's heads.

What cannot be underestimated is the value of support within the school setting, a context that regards seeking consultation as a strength rather than a weakness. Clearly any such an intervention needs to take place in consultation with parents, and in some boroughs it may involve the local Educational Psychology Service.

Questioning our own understanding

Finally, it is important to recognise the powerful emotions we may feel in seeing children suffer in this way, and how our own feelings of rage, loss or disappointment can make us less able to hear children's struggles and achievements. Rather than adhering to any pre-set guidelines, it is probably more useful to explore our personal understanding of children by asking:

- What have we learned from relating to children outside of our professional lives?
- What have we learned from our work with children in the other clinical contexts?
- What do we find most difficult in working with children?
- How could we change this, and do we need to observe or play with non-clinical children?
- What personal issues do we need to address to help us to listen to such pain, sadness or anger in children?

- How can play be used to strengthen children's voice within the family?
- How do we avoid being experienced as too intrusive?
- How can family sessions remain sufficiently child-focused to ensure they are meaningful to all family members?
- How do we pace differing needs within the room?
- How does gender, culture and race impact on our readiness to engage with children?

While these questions are far from all-inclusive, my experience has shown they provide a framework for individual professionals and teams to explore how beliefs about childhood affect clinical work.

Conclusions

This chapter has focused on the tremendous demands a child faces when someone in the family becomes seriously ill. Each child's experience will be influenced by the effect of the illness on other family members, on brothers, sisters, mothers and fathers. Attempts to protect one another mean that, all too often, ill and healthy family members attempt to hide their fears from one another. Children are at the very stage of life at which they are learning to understand the world around them, to make sense of roles both within and outside the family, so that, although well-intentioned, attempts to deny the reality of the child's experience can add to their confusion and lack of trust. While some undergo tremendous growth, in many families fears of death and damage mean their achievements and distress are not heard, particularly if unrelated to illness.

Although illness cannot be avoided, what we can attempt to ensure is that children have access to some relationship in which they are able to make sense of their experiences, to formulate a story that is about their own rather than others' experience. In this way, they can be helped to face the future with trust and confidence. This means recognising the centrality of family relationships in children's psychological development, the overwhelming evidence that experiences in childhood influence subsequent capacity to parent and the quality of emotional and social learning in sibling relationships. It is at the peril of the next generation that we ignore these children.

In our work with adults and children, it is time we added our questions and demands to their silent voices, to integrate treatment and prevention programmes with specific understanding of children's psychosocial needs. Whether or not this leads to interventions like designing leaflets or creating a space for children on adult units or hospices, it is essential that we examine how our own work systems could change to address the needs of children more effectively.

Summary

1. Serious physical illness has considerable impact on the lives of children, be the ill person a child, a parent or a sibling. However, focusing solely on pathology can limit our understanding of resilience and coping strategies, of protective factors mediating traumatic experiences.
2. Withholding information can harm rather than protect, but care needs to be taken in talking to children (practical recommendations were provided).
3. Children use play and non-verbal communication to portray what they cannot or do not want to say, but we need to guard against our attempts to make sense of their experience becoming intrusive.
4. The fears and frustrations evoked by illness can mean a loss of childhood, as children face limitations to their functioning, discrimination, and struggle to have their needs for autonomy or age-appropriate behaviour met.
5. When a sibling is ill, children face a double bind: to 'make up' for the illness without attempting to replace the sibling. The pressure to appear to cope inevitably affects how siblings negotiate support and rivalry.
6. When a parent is ill, clinical work focuses on helping children retain a sense of childhood, but respects the child's desire to care for the parent.
7. Crucial issues to consider in work with adolescents include the importance of physical appearance, and control factors in compliance and care-taking.
8. Increased attention is being placed on school-based interventions, but in order for this to work, schools need to provide additional support for teachers.
9. Exploring, extending and reconnecting with our personal understanding of childhood is crucial to ensuring our interactions with children are age-appropriate and respectful.

6

PARENTING AND CHRONIC ILLNESS

by Barbara Dale

This chapter gives an overview of issues related to being a parent who is sick or parenting a sick child. What is rarely recognised are the problems created for parenting when an adult is sick. Substantial case examples will be provided, illustrating the value of looking beyond illness when trying to understand family patterns. The families have agreed to these accounts being included.

Normal and chronic illness

Parenting a sick child is a normal family experience. All children are sometimes ill: some have periods of acute illness or are involved in accidents requiring hospitalisation. At these times most parents experience worry, shock and considerable demands on their resilience and patience. In emergencies, friends and family can be called on and are happy to respond to the crisis.

Parenting a child with chronic illness is different. Its long-term nature means that what is originally an emergency becomes almost normal or expected. Although the wider family may remain sympathetic, there is less expectation of particular attention.

Social isolation

Most families with children have busy lives. Families who cannot fit in because of special needs may feel excluded and disregarded. This may not be the intention, but is often families' experience. For example, babysitting is frequently arranged on an exchange basis. Few people are willing to take responsibility for a child needing medication, and parents often feel anxious about leaving ill children with inexperienced carers. Commonly, families live away from relatives, so extra resources are limited.

Illness culture: its advantages and risks

Support groups for parents of chronically ill children provide understanding and, in sharing a common experience, normalise some family anxiety and loneliness. Conversely, being drawn into the culture of illness can have an adverse affect, particularly for other children in the family. There may be considerable tension between receiving support and acceptance, while retaining space for relationships beyond illness.

Some families are more vulnerable to being drawn into an illness culture than others; there are parents for whom the warmth and friendship of a more closed community has an almost seductive quality. So great are needs rooted in earlier life experiences that their connection with this community may militate against the well-being of the child. The child can become almost required to remain ill so parents can remain within this group. Alarm signals for professionals may come as irritation about overemphasising the illness or minimising improvement. As our irritation can be a valuable indicator, the following questions can be useful to consider:

'What irritates me about this person/family?'
'Do I have any sense of disbelief about their presentation of illness?'

If the answer to the first question does not relate to the issues discussed above, we may need to consider whether the family's issues reflects similarities with our personal or professional lives. If we feel disbelief, we probably need to understand the family's life experiences prior to illness.

The demands of caring for a sick child can bring to the surface parents' own unmet needs. Where these become confused with the child's demands for care, separate provision may need to be made, like referral to a Child and Family Clinic. However, such a referral can only be successful where professionals are able to help the parents recognise their understandable vulnerability, rather than make them feel blamed.

Understanding the impact of family values on parenting

Understanding family values is crucial to establishing a collaborative approach between family and clinician, helping to avoid blame (Rolland, 1994). This creates the sense of exploring together rather than acting as judge. This is essential, as medical interviews are often experienced as dissatisfying, particularly when the search for a diagnosis has been prolonged.

Rolland expressed surprise at families' full responses when asked about beliefs. Families are most likely to become engaged in seeking help when they feel truly heard. This is not just about describing the problem, but includes beliefs: why they, in this family, think the problem exists for them. How this information is understood influences the future changes the family feels able to make. Beliefs that cause shame and guilt can control parents' freedom to see themselves as competent, or appropriate care-givers.

Patterson and McCubbin (1985) stress that our work should be future oriented rather than reflect on history. This is probably rooted in the assumption that history is antithetical to a future oriented and optimistic approach. However, revisiting the past may underpin the freedom to face the future. To achieve this, we need to help families recognise how actions, based on beliefs, are intended to help even when their effect may have been the opposite.

CASE EXAMPLE

In a family where the son, aged 14, was friendless, overanxious and immature, the mother's illness beliefs were central. As a child, her family suffered extreme poverty. There was violence between her parents, and her brother died from leukaemia. She therefore believed her central parental role was to be watchful of her child, something she felt her brother had lacked. When her son was younger, watchfulness took the form of engagement in any school activity that allowed parental involvement. At senior school, there were fewer opportunities for parental involvement. This redirected her watchfulness into vigilance about his health, keeping him home at any suggestion of illness. Frequently absent from school, he dropped out of his learning and peer group, becoming increasingly dependent on his mother just when peers were establishing greater independence, increasing his difference.

Intrinsic to exploring history was ensuring his mother did not experience blame for her watchfulness (Dale and Emerson, 1994). Understanding why she was watchful and recognising that all parents inevitably draw on personal experience, she was able to explore how watchfulness could be continued without limiting his opportunities to develop. In many ways, her earlier watchfulness enhanced his education and helped the school and other pupils. It had, however, decreased her opportunity to experience her son and herself developing greater independence. Had they, with their vulnerable history, been exposed to serious illness, their coping mechanisms could have been seriously impeded.

Normalising exceptional circumstances can have a liberating effect: being able to describe that, given her experience, watchfulness was important, proved a way of reframing her experience. However, it needed an authentic ring: the normal aspect was being watchful; its development into keeping her son at home moved the behaviour into being problematic. Disentangling these parts allowed her to own these explanations, and redefine the problem current solutions were creating.

Stress in families with a chronically ill child

Considerable interest has been shown in the stresses of families facing childhood illness (see Patterson and McCubbin, 1985, and Kazak and Nachman, 1991, for extended analysis), highlighting areas of stress such as:

- strained family relationships;
- limitations on family activities and goals;
- increased tasks and time commitment;
- increased financial burdens;
- housing adaptation;
- social isolation;
- medical concerns, particularly about the competence of care;
- different school experiences;
- grieving.

Of these, grieving can be most complicated for parents, particularly at life stages when developmental delay is most apparent: parents face grieving for the lost healthy child and sharing the child's grief, whilst having to maintain some optimism about the future. Giving families support in this process is of the greatest importance.

Where the child is treated as 'normal', their difference has to remain within them. If parents deny this inner sense of difference, children's ability to learn from experience becomes limited, often resulting in low self-esteem and resultant problems. The balance between recognising difference and what is normal is the greatest challenge to parenting ill children. Where the family can establish adaptive coping patterns that retain family life, the well-being of all members is enhanced.

Changing roles as mothers and fathers

In families where solutions to the child's care have resulted in the father playing a more active role, there are frequently changes in couple relationships. Fathers' increased care activity is often evident in organisational changes, like setting limits and rules, and practical provision. Uncertainty is a constant factor in long-term illness, so certainty about rules and limits can be reassuring and calming. Emotional responses frequently change too, with a reduction of aggressive or overly assertive behaviour.

Assertiveness in spouse relationships

A common pattern in couple relationships is women's acquiescence to men in decision-making, so women do not see themselves as holders of knowledge and decisions. As mothers are usually the main carers of sick children, they become the experts on illness, the holders of knowledge and decision-making. This increased status, combined with reduced aggression and anger in fathers, can substantially affect spouse and parenting relationships. Fathers' willingness to be less assertive, either physically or verbally, and mothers' increased sense of self-esteem, can contribute to better couple relationships and an enhanced emotional environment for the whole family. However, this should not be overvalued: the profound sense of guilt, blame and despair so often evident can counteract these advantages.

Parents protecting professionals

Parents can be sensitive to professionals' feelings and avoid topics they think might upset us. Professionals with whom families have a long-standing relationship often become central to their surviving and living with illness. It may seem important to safeguard that relationship, rather than express concerns that may jeopardise this relationship. Consultation is critical where professionals experience intense demands: it is unwise to assume we are 'all right'. All long-term work with chronically ill children or parents should include opportunities for consultation as a protective measure for professionals and families alike.

The following cases illustrate how these themes emerge in clinical work, first where the child is ill and then where the parent is ill.

Direct work with families

Parenting an ill child

This example demonstrates the importance of working at the family's pace. Allowing the work to go slowly enabled us to appreciate how hard these parents had worked to find a solution. On the face of it, the problems could seem simple: the parents needed to be less anxious, more involved in their daughter's school, less critical, more supportive of each other and accepting of difference. However, to have moved too quickly would have obstructed revealing their story, which provided a different explanation of their situation.

Respecting parents' competence is more than a professional stance: underpinning this work is my belief that, in most families, parents try to do their best. If they have problems they will have tried many, many solutions before seeking help from me. For that reason, we need to give them time to tell their story in their own way. Working slowly can be frustrating: families often want direct advice and solutions. What helps parents tolerate the delay whilst their story is explored is a secure base in therapy (Byng-Hall, 1995), a base which includes a sense of connection and respect for their parenting commitment.

These parents were resourceful, committed and imaginative. If practical solutions were going to solve the problem, they would have found them: rather, there were other factors that interfered with their freedom to resolve the difficulties themselves.

CASE EXAMPLE

The family referred themselves because they were concerned that their daughter (14 years old) lacked confidence, had few friends, was small for her years and unhappy. They mentioned as an aside that she had suffered from a thyroid deficiency since the age of 10, which was treated with medication. Monica was the eldest of four children. The others performed well academically and presented no particular concerns about forming relationships with friends or within the family.

Her parents' concerns focused on Monica's shyness, and the difficulty this created for relationships at home and school. She was considered isolated, unusually silent, lacking in energy and initiative. Both parents felt upset, unhappy and fearful that their attempts to encourage and stimulate her had been of no help. Initially, they made no links with her medical condition: it presented no problems and she managed her medication successfully.

Professional decisions about pace

Initially, sessions were slow, providing the family with little new information. There seemed to be an underlying sadness, frustration, disappointment and anger at feeling powerless to make things different. Monica remained fairly quiet and found constructing complete sentences difficult, sometimes impossible. She rarely spoke spontaneously, seemingly anxious, making constant eye checks with her parents, particularly her mother, and frequently lapsing into silence.

Separating layers and addressing the sense of failure

Frequently, circumstances develop which, if unresolved, become connected to quite unrelated new events in family life. Once this connection has been established, the explanation of the new event is forgotten and becomes attached to unresolved problems, even though quite separate. Our work involves disentangling different layers of information, and how this relates to each family's beliefs and values.

Monica experienced herself as a failure, so much that she feared completing sentences in case they were misunderstood or wrong. Her parents saw themselves as failures: whatever they did failed with Monica, but worked with their other children. This left them feeling frustrated, angry and sad. Monica felt responsible for her parents' experience, compounding difficulties.

Refocusing on illness

Therapy does not have definite answers: any explanation is one of many possibilities. Its usefulness lies in its fits with the family. Over the sessions, the importance of the thyroid condition re-emerged. Examining how they experienced her thyroid condition highlighted how painful this had been for them all.

The diagnosis came when her mother consulted her doctor because she was concerned that Monica, like herself, might stop growing when her menstruation started. From the family's description, all discussion focused on the present condition and medication plans for the future. It was suggested the condition could have been present from birth. On learning about this, Monica was able to relate them to her lack of balance. Once medication was established, the family put the problem to one side.

Use of metaphors to link behaviour

I introduced the idea of balance as a metaphor for the way Monica and her parents experienced her problems. From early childhood, Monica's mother was aware she had little confidence. As she was her first child, she found it hard to judge what to expect. In retrospect, as an experienced mother, she could see Monica had always been physically tentative. Her parents never found themselves having to hold her back as happened with their exuberant, younger children. Monica's sister, Jane, three years her junior, was a lively child, whose strong demands quickly took centre stage in family life. During therapy, Jane became increasingly sensitive to this, and although gifted with ready answers, trained herself to give space to Monica rather than answer for her.

Both parents recalled that activities like walking along a wall and jumping down, enjoyable to other children, had been a challenge to Monica. She had needed a hand to help her: there was an uncertainty, a wobble, but not sufficient for them to ask for help. There were many strands to this tentative sense for Monica: her sense of permanence was different from other children, she could not be sure things would remain still or that she could rely on herself, and looked to others to help. As she came from an active, eloquent family, help was always at hand, with voices ever ready to talk for her. Her mother recalled her perpetual uncertainty about responding to Monica. She tried many ways but nothing seemed to make a difference, creating a gap between them. Her mother could never feel she had been a good enough parent and Monica was never able to feel a good enough daughter. A sense of sadness became attached to Monica. Her parents experienced this as a criticism of themselves, resulting in frustration and anger.

The destructiveness of uncertainty

Their experiences with their younger, talkative children highlighted how certain parenting styles had proved unhelpful with Monica. The parents had learned to second guess what might be important for Monica: although they sometimes got it wrong, they recognised her difference from their other children. While they found it hard to be confident of their parenting, it did mean Monica remained in focus. Without their efforts to second guess, she could have slipped from view. Two styles of parenting developed: one for talkative, gregarious and demanding children and one for a child who was silent, shy, inactive and had few, if any friends. Although these differences became more apparent as the children matured, the parents remained hopeful that Monica would grow out of her shyness.

Respect for parents

Monica's parents were active and serious about parenting, family life being central to their happiness. However, they did not feel supported by their wider family, who responded with suggestions of treating Monica differently. As they felt they had tried all possibilities, these suggestions seemed like criticisms and misunderstandings grew. The parents continued to experience distress and guilt, with Monica's father feeling he could only see his faults in Monica.

Soon after diagnosis, the family had lived abroad for two years. During that time Monica became more relaxed, made friends and the parents were relieved she was growing out of her shyness. This was a more relaxed, confident time for all the family: everyone had been different, not just Monica. Returning to Britain confronted them with many problems, and they tended to drop their new approaches and adopted traditional roles. This often happens when life is difficult: it is simplest to go by rules you know even if they create difficulties. Monica slipped back into the role she had only tentatively escaped. However, the parents were more confident: they knew life could be different and sought help.

Isolation, vulnerability and family strength

While Monica felt powerless to fulfil her parents' wishes, they in turn felt powerless to make her happy. Their vulnerability meant any comment from their wider family hurt deeply, whatever the intention, increasing their isolation. The more they felt to blame, the harder it became to seek help. Monica saw herself as 'bad news' and kept away from people to protect them, resulting in few opportunities to make friends. The sisters tried to be friends, but as they grew older and games depended more on verbal interplay, this became difficult.

However, they were determined to find a new way of relating. This meant progress often felt too slow for them, but it did give them the push to seek solutions. The parents' concern for Monica and her enjoyment has been crucial to the changes that have occurred, and they are now beginning to feel greater respect for themselves. Monica has shown courage in challenging her anxieties and is establishing new friendships and a picture of herself as someone who can do things. She is a kind and gentle person her family can now enjoy and value.

Staying open to different explanations

The family felt that recognising the impact of her condition provided a different explanation for many worries they have had over her life. They also appreciated that, although extremely important, this was but one explanation: other circumstances in their lives, not referred to here, provide alternative ways of understanding difficulties. Looking back, Monica's mother felt that had a health-care professional asked whether she had concerns about Monica, her worries would have been legitimised, enabling her to address her concerns earlier.

Writing an account like this can make everything sound neat. That is not the case: the family still have many important issues to consider and resolve.

What it means when a parent is ill

CASE EXAMPLE

In this family the mother is ill and her twin daughters are responsible for much of the care. One daughter had a congenital heart defect, but was advised it was no longer a problem prior to our first contact. Here, the focus will be on an adult's need to be heard as a parent when facing illness. Today, one in three families have lone parents, so the circumstances facing families when a lone parent is chronically sick should be of serious concern to us all.

Dazzle factors and avoiding pain

Whereas in the first family there was a risk of initially thinking the problems presented were simple, here they appeared overwhelming. Some problems can seem so large and dazzling that we can assume they account for all difficulties. In this situation, Motor Neurone Disease (MND) is such a dreadful illness that it was hard for us to think beyond it and allow other themes to surface. Facing terminal illness is deeply painful. Looking back, I recognise that, despite intending not to shirk this pain, time and again I moved sideways rather than approach it fully, although my colleague drew my attention to this. Concerns about pacing how we face the full pain of illness can mirror similar ambiguity within the family, deterring them from exploring their fears.

If you are at home, are you 'really ill'?

MND is a condition which is almost entirely treated at home until the patient becomes unable to cope. This can bring confusion; if the illness can be treated at home, is it really serious? This may mean family members change their approach to the patient more slowly, and the dynamics may be more intense if the parent who is ill is a lone parent.

Our initial contact was an eloquent letter from the mother explaining she had MND and felt her daughters, aged 14, were finding it hard to understand or talk to her about her illness. What gradually emerged, as we got to know the family, was that her daughters' approach to her illness was to minimise it in every way. They tried to maximise aspects of their mother that could be seen as 'normal' with the hope this would keep her strong and optimistic about the future. Although they had older sisters, there was no other adult living in the household, so day-to-day care had to be provided by them.

Independence: a hidden obstacle

Over her lifetime the mother, Alice had challenged her own low self-esteem, allowing herself to move from feeling she had to submit to demands, to experiencing herself as more independent. She was deeply saddened she had not learned to be a different sort of parent for her older daughters but was determined to be different with the twins. Valuing independence as a central tenet of her parenting became intensely problematic as her illness progressed.

The development of independence in young people in their teens presents most parents with a challenge. In many ways, it is a paradox: the message to young people is to be independent, but do as I say. Most parents try to overcome this by a negotiation which respects young people's views, but with the expectation that even if they disagree, they should maintain household rules. Although the degree to which household rules are challenged varies, causing them to be strongly or loudly stated, few families pass unscathed through this time.

Dilemmas about independence became connected with Alice's health and their inevitable role reversal, with Chàrlotte and Louisa alternating as carer and daughters. Alice's wish to respect their views and increasing independence became linked with the girls' concern to keep their mother 'normal' in order to keep her healthy. This showed particularly over use of aids such as wheelchairs, walking frames, or altering the house to accommodate her increased disability. Whilst Alice saw her wish to use a wheelchair as improving her quality of life, increasing her mobility and opportunity to join in family life, for her daughters it was the opposite. It went against their idea of 'normal', of keeping healthy by walking.

Finding and losing voice: taking sides

Alice described how she had fought to increase her sense of self-esteem and had, despite dreadful life experiences, found her 'voice' and strength, only to have it taken from her by her illness. Whilst in a sitting position, her voice was the most tangible evidence of illness. Although her daughters were still able to understand their mother, Alice's speech was extremely indistinct, creating opportunities for misunderstanding or not hearing. Since these are frequently a foundation for disagreement between parents and teenagers, difficulties in negotiation were intense. They sometimes didn't want to hear their mother's voice because its sound was tangible evidence of her illness. This made it hard to hear the content of her speech, particularly when it clashed with their wish for increased independence.

Part of our work was to put the therapist's voice alongside Alice's voice, so her words as parent could be clearly heard. This is an unusual manoeuvre: it would be more common to give space to parents views rather than speak for them. However, in this instance, the mother's illness undermined her position as a parent and she needed the experience of another adult taking her side.

Loss of childhood

As a consequence of their mother's health, her daughters had lurched from childhood to adulthood without time for rehearsal. As the twins got taller and stronger, what had been family games developed an unpleasant side to them. Charlotte, who was the older twin and the one most central as carer and organiser of the household, found herself 'playing' by pinching and pushing her mother. On being asked to stop, she didn't 'hear'. Ultimately, Alice shouted and hit out with her sticks. Louisa, the younger twin, stayed out of the 'game' but was critical of her sister.

All were very upset by this, but for Charlotte it was particularly undermining. She had dismissed her feelings of resentment at having to care for her mother, and the inevitable isolation from peers which child carers experience. That would have meant acknowledging how much illness had deprived her of the mother she had known and how bleak the future could seem. In the saddest possible way, Charlotte was criticised for being a child and over-doing the 'game', yet criticised for being an adult and in charge of the 'game'.

Professional competence

Understanding Charlotte's fear of sadness changed the story of the 'game'. I took responsibility for holding on to the idea of her sadness until she was ready to do that herself. As professionals, it is important we find ways of holding on to our professional competence. Families often want us to give up knowing something because it is too painful. At such times, it can be useful to say 'I'll have to keep that in my mind because it keeps coming back to me.' With Charlotte's sadness, this kept the subject present but did not dictate the pace at which it was accepted. Charlotte needed to keep her strength: it was important not to demand changes until she and the family were ready, by which time they had other ways of coping.

Linking past problems with present difficulties

Louisa, the younger twin, was born with a heart defect. She had weighed just 3 lbs at birth, and had been tube-fed for five months. Alice had hoped to emphasise Louisa's healthy side but, over time, continuing fears about Louisa's health meant she was influenced by other family members and began treating Louisa differently. Charlotte had become Louisa's protector at school, so training her for her more adult role when her mother later became ill. When they were first seen, although Louisa would make a contribution, Charlotte and Alice often continued as though she hadn't spoken. Louisa in turn frequently daydreamed, mishearing what was said to her, or not.

Just knowing something is happening can be sufficient to make changes; but where a pattern of relating has a close fit with other issues within the family, change is more complicated. By having a small, almost unheard voice, Louisa remained more childlike for her years. In a situation where Alice felt overpowered by illness and at times by Charlotte, having a daughter who allowed her to feel like a mother was very special. For Charlotte, having a sister, particularly a twin, who looked up to her, depended upon her and was always there to be her friend, was an immense comfort. Precarious adjustment to her carer's role meant she never allowed herself to give way to the sadness and depression she so frequently felt. The opportunity to be vigorous in defence of her sister at school gave her some opportunity to vent the angry feelings her depressions engendered. Remaining more child-like removed Louisa from the carer role or recognising the extent of her mother's illness. However, this was at the cost of her freedom to explore and learn, creating considerable disadvantage at school.

Understanding how patterns developed enabled us to think about each aspect separately, rather than as caused by and connected to Alice's illness.

Family solutions to independence

The family found a unique solution to learning independence when it wasn't possible for Alice to be in charge in the usual way. It also helped the twins to have a wider social life and to respect each other differently: they bought a puppy and took up dog training. The initiative for dog training classes came from Charlotte, who was concerned about the mess Buttercup, the puppy, made at home. This was fully supported by Alice, who saw that it gave the twins an interest outside the home and the social life she wanted for them but could not provide. Although Buttercup was owned by both girls, Louisa held back, was less central in the training and consequently less responded to by Buttercup. Charlotte enjoyed working with Buttercup, and training classes provided opportunities to enter competitions. Buttercup was remarkably successful at competing: Charlotte had learned the importance of consistent command and encouragement rather than being overbearing. Although Louisa was sometimes responsible for showing Buttercup in competitions, her voice rarely had sufficient command to ensure co-operation. So. Charlotte became more in charge of Buttercup and Louisa's voice remained unheard.

The school: fears of illness being seen

Parallel with dog training, Alice become more proactive about her daughters' school. In the past, she had visited their school and they had understood enough to send written notes home to which she could write in reply. The twins were anxious about their mother going to their school. They were embarrassed that her illness would make them different, and that when she spoke to teachers she would become emotional and cry. Neither girl cried in the sessions until a long way into therapy. Alice however, frequently became very tearful, apparently justifying her daughters' concern about school. Alice found a solution to the school visit, enlisting the help of an older daughter to attend Parents Evening with her. She translated what Alice had to say to these teachers. This relieved Charlotte and Louisa of having to be present but ensured Alice was heard by the teaching staff. It also meant not giving in to her daughters' demands, emphasising that, as their mother, her views may not coincide with theirs, modelling independence through difference.

By now, they were involved in their GCSEs. Alice took the opportunity to increase the priority placed on school work rather than housework, and to explore extended care from outside the home. Until then, Charlotte in particular had been adamant that this was not needed. With the help of the MND Society worker, Alice helped Charlotte, Louisa and the older daughter who had subsequently become more involved to increase their knowledge of the disease, and of the care that would be needed and available. Alice increasingly used therapy to establish plans and to differentiate roles within the family.

Whilst initially it was important to support Alice by voicing parental issues, it now became important to draw back and allow Alice's voice to be heard alone.

Developments for the family

Louisa developed greater independence and became increasingly active in her learning, sharing more fully in household duties. Charlotte no longer felt so overly in charge, and had more time for school work. She and Louisa have a growing social life, as does Alice independently from them. Louisa now has her own dog and they recognise that it was confusing for Buttercup to be given commands by two such different people.

Alice's illness is progressing, though slower than she was led to expect. Stephen Hawking's life and challenge to illness has made an enormous contribution to her outlook. Her daughters are more able to talk about plans for their future when their mother's illness becomes more severe. While previous attempts to ignore the illness paradoxically meant it had subsumed all else, they have been able to step outside the illness and not let it be the description of all their lives. Alice is able to be both mother and patient, and Charlotte and Louisa are more age-appropriate daughters and carers.

Pace: holding the dying and living in mind

Throughout the work, the family showed considerable courage in remaining involved. Therapy is a painful exercise: in the presence of such pain, it is understandable that one tries to avoid more. One of the issues we as therapists have to recognise, when working with a life threatening illness in the family, is pace. Time has a very different meaning for Alice who is unlikely to have enough, than it has for her daughters. There have been times when Alice prompted me to speed up and be more challenging. My holding back has been partly influenced by her daughters' pace but also by my own reluctance to face the terminal nature of the illness.

I have had to learn to hold the uneven balance of the different pace they needed. This is an uncomfortable position to be in. Health-care professionals who do not include the issue of being a parent in their thinking or discussion can be unaware of the conflicts of interest between being a parent and patient. In Alice's case, her health and well-being was intimately connected to her role as a mother: she could not exercise her right to a wheelchair until her role as a mother was re-established.

Conclusions

These cases embody issues of empowerment. The loss of self-esteem parents experience, whether as patients or parents of the patient, can have a disabling effect on all children. As health-care professionals, we have the opportunity to influence family decisions: our discussions with parents are often endowed with a special level of importance, and listened to with extra attention, creating even small opportunities to address parenting.

Given appropriate support, families can make substantial changes in behaviour that not only benefit the member who is ill, but change the emotional climate for all family members. Looking at families from a systems perspective highlights how relationships may enhance or hinder aspirations for the well-being of all family members.

Work with these families happened over a considerable number of sessions, and I had the benefit of working with a co-worker

(Jenny Altschuler). Most professionals will not have this amount of time with families, or the opportunity to co-work. It may be useful to have the idea of a co-worker in your head with some sort of check list of central issues to consider, such as those summarised below.

Summary

1. Behaviour patterns may have more to do with how the family functioned before the illness than the process of the illness itself.
2. Most families are normal families with a sick member, rather than families who are fundamentally different.
3. Family beliefs can result in being unable to change habits, even when unhelpful, until they are understood differently.
4. Central to our work is the commitment to avoiding blame and working collaboratively when seeking to understand family beliefs.
5. There can be gains, not just loss: differences between men and women as parents may be reconciled in a new way in the face of illness.
6. Parents' own experience of parenting is of fundamental importance, whether they or their child is a patient.
7. Delay in diagnosis can result in changes in behaviour that go unrecognised: this can continue to distort family behaviour once the diagnosis is made.
8. Professionals finding themselves unusually frustrated or upset by a family may need to ask themselves some questions about their own experience and beliefs: are the similarities between themselves and the family such that the problem for the family is also a problem for them?

7

WORKING WITH ADULTS WHO ARE ILL

A diagnosis of illness can have a profound effect on how we view our lives, influencing relationships with families, friends and colleagues. Major alterations in lifestyle may be required to prevent the likelihood of symptoms recurring. Countless losses may evolve, challenging the denial of vulnerability, fallibility and lack of control so prevalent in our society today: tremendous feelings of fear, guilt, regrets, worries about other people's reactions and concerns about coping with treatment may be evoked.

As adults, it means negotiating a whole range of contradictions in identity, integrating a concept of self as someone who needs care with the concept of being an individual in one's own right: a mother, father, daughter or partner, responsible for the physical and emotional well-being of others. This raises dilemmas of balancing family responsibilities with personal needs for care, of finding a way of maintaining intimacy, separateness and dignity while giving or receiving the care serious illness demands.

While diagnosis, prognosis and treatment provide clues as to what may be demanded from us, expectations and beliefs about illness and loss are central in determining:

- how we face physical, emotional and cognitive deterioration in ourselves and others;
- how we negotiate shifts in rules about personal boundaries and intimacy;
- whether we allow ourselves to be cared for by others, to prioritise our needs over those of other family members;
- how we cope with uncertainty;
- how we maintain a sense of continuity and hope.

Solutions which seem helpful at any one time will probably vary as the illness and quite unrelated life circumstances alter. Rather than providing answers, this chapter raises some of the dilemmas presented, encouraging readers to consider their own expectations of personal health responsibility as adults.

How does the life cycle affect adults' responses?

At any stage of life, illness presents not only the possibility of loss but scope to reassess lifestyles, with each transition posing a new dilemma. As family members age and mature, shifts in relationships take place, with the family system accommodating to the changing needs of its members. This means that, in working with adults, we need to consider what disease means at their specific stage of life.

For example, at 20 or 30, the onset of illness can raise painful questions of how personal health affects child-rearing, about the capacity to conceive, risks of pregnancy to a partner's or child's health, and the probability children will witness parents' deterioration or death while young. As physically, the illness affects only one partner in a couple, it can become complicated for healthy partners to voice their own views, as if responsibility for child-bearing lies with one person. However, decisions like these affect the hopes and future of both members of a couple. While practical solutions like artificial insemination, surrogacy and adoption may be available, the psychological implications for each person may be different.

Where illness strikes in a parent with small children, considerable care is required to ensure child-focused needs are met. The story need not only be one of deficit: illness presents the opportunity for children to learn compassion, sensitivity and trust in adults outside the family, skills that will prove important as they mature. However, anxieties about what the illness means to children can remain, affecting parents' ability to prioritise their own needs when feeling unwell.

Care-taking poses quite different issues when illness strikes in old age. Although we probably view illness and death as more likely in later years, the pain, shock, regrets, sadness and anger experienced by family members may be no less. In some situations, an ill person can be cared for by a partner with minimal additional support. However, not all elderly people have partners, and at this stage of life partners are themselves often frail. Frequently, then, illness in one partner means that either one or both are moved into supervised residential or nursing accommodation. So, in addition to facing illness, they both face the loss of their home, and independence.

Decisions about such transitions raise tremendous feelings of ambivalence in extended family members. Frequently decisions about additional care relate to the support the extended family can provide. Adult children may come forward to care for their ill parent. This can be profoundly satisfying, providing a way of reconnecting or even resolving past hurts and disappointments. However, this relative reversal of roles can prove complicated to manage. Unsupported, the practical demands of ongoing care can rob an elderly relative of dignity or overburden adult children who have their own child-rearing and/or career commitments.

Inevitably, how families negotiate change at each life stage is determined by both the ill person and the rest of the family, by the quality of relationships that existed prior to the illness, and the reciprocal support the actual patient is able to give to their carers. In our work with families, we need to consider members' positions in the life cycle and help them balance their commitments to look after others with their own needs for support.

Accommodating to change

Clinical and research reviews (Kleinman, 1988; Watson *et al.*, 1991; Radley, 1994) have highlighted the psychological distress serious physical illness can create for adults. It appears that *illness-related factors*, such as the severity of physical symptoms and prognosis, and *psychosocial coping resources*, like social support and sense of control, influence reactions and adaptation at each stage of a disease.

Just as healthy family members, particularly partners, influence how patients come to terms with illness or recover from surgery, studies also emphasise the physical and emotional distress experienced by other family members. Sometimes the partners' distress mirrors or surpasses that of the ill person, so they form an unacknowledged population at risk (Ell *et al.*, 1988; Keitl *et al.*, 1990). The complexity of care-giving means that the *stage* of a disease can be more central to the psychological well-being of healthy rather than ill partners: symptoms and role limitations alter demands placed on ill people, but also affect the care, support and intimacy available to healthy partners.

Highlighting this distress has undoubtedly added impetus to extending psychosocial support. However, inadvertently it can lead us to focus on pathology, on how people 'fail', rather than what enables people to manage painful and unpredictable life events. This is what we need to integrate clinically: interest in what helps adults and their families adapt, what efforts reduce stress in difficult situations (problem-focused coping) and how emotional aspects of their situation are addressed (emotion-focused coping). Styles of coping described amongst cancer patients are beginning to influence psychosocial treatment (Greer and Silberfarb, 1982). These include:

- *anxious preoccupation*: 'I worry constantly another lump is growing and ask my partner to check daily in case another one has developed';
- *denial*: 'This is just a lump, not cancer';
- *fighting spirit*: 'I'm going to fight this: cancer isn't going to beat me';
- *stoic acceptance*: 'I'm going to have to live with this';
- *helpless/hopeless*: 'There's nothing I can do, it's the end of my life'.

Already, categories like these are used as a guide to identifying patients considered most at risk: cognitive behavioural techniques are employed to teach ill people a fighting attitude to illness (Moorey, 1991). However, as evidence that attitude can of itself influence the course of a condition is far from clear, insensitive application of these ideas can be damaging: they may unwittingly pathologise cancer sufferers, implying personal 'failure' to avert the course of the condition, heightening self-blame, questioning sick roles and adding to the burden faced.

Successful coping can also not be achieved outright, once and for all: how we cope one day may have little bearing on how we will cope the next. The very concept of 'successful coping' is variable. It is uncertain what this means to us at any one time: we could argue that continuing with daily life regardless of a life-threatening illness qualifies as coping well. But we could also say this fails to take account of changed circumstances, unnecessarily endangering health and burdening others with anxiety we cannot face ourselves.

Making sense of the illness

Most current psychosocial research on illness is based on professionals' assessment, on the scientist/outsider's account. As the detection of emotional difficulties by health professionals is notoriously poor (Maguire, 1985), we may be developing but one interpretation of this multi-faceted experience. Both in research and clinically, we are beginning to pay greater respect to what 'insiders' say, how ill people and their families talk of their experiences, rather than making assumptions from a relatively 'outside' perspective. This involves listening carefully to how illness stories are told and change; the coherence of their accounts; how links between one event and another are orchestrated, what is stressed or minimised; how personal struggles relate to wider social and cultural influences; and how the language used portrays self-identity: whether people describe themselves in the first person, owning their experience, or use phrases like 'one thinks', or 'one may . . .' to distance themselves from this.

Many of these accounts describe illness as a *disempowering disruption* (Bury, 1982), leaving little sense of being able to connect with their pre-illness identity. They tell how the daily life of being ill, the *social isolation* and perception of being a 'burden' impacts on self-concept, undermining the process of normalisation.

Faced with similar demands, we find very different ways of making sense of our experience: some stories resemble professional accounts of illness while others are quite different, telling of a frightening and humiliating loss of control and personal respect. Still others talk of how, after the initial horror, illness enabled cherished dreams to be realised and relationships to be positively reconstructed.

Access to social support, a sense of personal control and relationships prior to the illness are the main catalysts in this process. Important, too, is how we interpret any condition: for example, one man with multiple sclerosis reported that his divorce helped him to retain his positive masculine identity rather than describing it in terms of loss, incapacity and ill health (Reissman, 1990).

What is valid for one family member may be less so for the next. Members may give different accounts of negotiating blame, stigma and ambiguity. Many stories highlight struggles to legitimise their suffering and hold on to moral competence in a context that associates moral values with health. Others grapple to retain intimacy and separateness in the face of the increased care-taking demands the disability creates (Parker, 1993).

Respecting uniqueness means valuing personal accounts in our assessments and interventions. All clinical interviews, be they medical consultations or occupational therapy sessions, provide a context for sharing and reconstructing what is unique to biographies. We all select from several options in deciding how to talk, moving between options to make points which then become the dominant way of viewing that experience. For example, a man's narrative of his cancer may include stories that highlight disruption to masculinity, adequacy as a father or financial provider. His wife's or partner's story of what the illness means to her is often less readily included in their apparently shared narrative: how his incapacity led her to discover her own competence, or how the emotions evoked by the illness rekindled an intimacy long absent from their relationship.

What does illness mean to an adult's sense of self?

Focusing on how identity unfolds in the stories told can help families re-edit their story, selecting previously ignored options. Where the condition is ignored and creates difficulties, this may mean identifying and attending to metaphors that signify loss or damage. Elsewhere, it may mean listening for how these stories enhance a sense of self that is competent and can have feelings *despite* being labelled a patient. While this does not mean denying loss or pain, it can provide a way of shifting from a narrative of dependency and victimisation to one of greater agency and control. A non-judgemental context in which these experiences can be 're-storied' in the presence of those intrinsic to members' sense of self helps families to normalise what can feel frightening and bewildering. Whilst consultation soon after diagnosis can provide a forum for family members to share some of the feelings aroused, this can sometimes feel too soon. Clearly, this is no one-way process: therapeutic interventions play a part, but the initiative and courage to consider change lies with each and every family member.

Illness inevitably alters our constructions of ourselves: diet, exercise and lifestyle may be prescribed, demanding changes in the timing and flexibility of our most intimate personal habits. Our psychosexual image may be affected by the physical incapacitation or scarring accompanying the diseases or treatment: exposing one's body to the scrutiny of others compounds this, accentuating the loss of a predictable way of relating to self and others.

Illness can be viewed as a series of *disruptive events*, during which the structures and very forms of knowledge that underpin daily life are changed: the world of pain and suffering, formerly only a distant possibility, becomes a reality; rules of reciprocity and mutual support alter. Self-worth closely linked to being an effective or creative professional in the world of work is challenged. Common-sense assumptions about how to behave lose their usefulness, but alternatives are not readily apparent. People may feel unsure what behaviour is legitimate in these changed circumstances, unsure how much to disclose to a partner, to friends or a GP. Being unable to carry out practical and material tasks changes relationships between oneself and others, and can lead to a deep sense of embarrassment: the scope for individualism, capacity for reflection and even manipulation of personal appearance can be disrupted by being less able to mobilise personal resources.

Our sense of who we are relates not only to experiences but to personal reflections about ourselves. The thoughts, feelings and premises that inform personal narratives are not static: they are continually shaped and reshaped by experiences and interactions with the outside world. Today, we are all exposed to somewhat contradictory assumptions of how to live our lives, contradictions which vary according to gender, race and religion. For example, in Britain, women are expected to achieve self-worth from working outside the home, while remaining central care-givers in family life. They may be expected to play a subservient position in one context and to act with independence and authority in the next. While men's sense of self is more firmly connected to work outside the home, they are expected to play a greater role in care-taking within the home, with little anticipation of how this affects role clarity or how couples negotiate rivalry.

Life is rarely free from contradictions: the challenge lies in finding a way of living with yet another set of complex contradictions. Our response will be influenced by what this means for ourselves and others, for family members, friends and colleagues. Some relationships will have begun when the ill person was already affected, but in many cases illness strikes after a relationship has been established for many years. This means having to discover new ways of relating and viewing the future within the context of a past. This past may have embraced hurt and disappointment in one another, influencing whether shifts in behaviour can be viewed as legitimate. Whether working individually, with couples or families, it is the challenge to definition of self in relationships that is central to helping adults broaden the options that lie ahead.

CASE EXAMPLE

Self-image can be particularly disrupted where the condition follows a slowly deteriorating, intermittent course, where what we or others can expect of us varies from day to day. A 36-year-old woman with MND sought consultation about what this meant to her children. Her definition of herself had become totally subsumed by her condition: she spoke of herself as a bag of useless bones, who had to be wheeled about like a baby. She felt angry, resentful, confused and ambivalent about her role as wife and mother. On the one hand, she felt pressured to maintain household chores, yet felt unsure of her ability to do so. This accentuated her ambivalence about being able to retain parenting tasks, such as supervising homework. Uncertainty about what she could physically manage was rendered more complicated by her sense that her husband no longer found her attractive.

She repeatedly stressed her husband and children would not attend the clinic, so was seen alone for several sessions. In addressing her initial concerns about parenting, it was important to confront what the disease meant for her own self-image. This included discussing what the physical changes meant to her, and the fear and anger she and her family felt about how she had changed. However, as important as exploring the impact of her increased incapacitation on relationships was challenging the effect of her own altered self-image on the value she placed on her expertise as mother and wife. Exploring and deconstructing what being a mother meant to her enabled her to resume some of the tasks she felt were beyond her grasp, including helping her children face her illness. As her religious beliefs emphasised an acceptance of fate, interventions were framed in terms of acceptance, that accepting fate included accepting her ongoing position as a mother. This had a tremendous impact on her sense of self, but it remains unclear whether this enabled her to introduce a similar change in her relationship with her husband.

What might illness mean for couple relationships?

Although this section focuses largely on couple relationships, many of the issues raised here will be applicable to ill people who, at the time of diagnosis, are not in ongoing long-term relationships, or where the relationships most affected by illness are with extended family members, adult children or friends. While most of the literature on adult relationships focuses on married partners, many people we encounter personally and professionally are in permanent, intimate relationships but not legally married. The term 'partner' rather than 'spouse' is therefore used here.

In choosing a partner, either as heterosexual or homosexual couples, we make deliberate choices but are probably also unconscious of many qualities that attract us to one another. Some of us are attracted by difference in attitudes, in competence or expectations, while others find difference less appealing. Some attempt to submerge their personality in the other, while the reverse is true for others. We vary in how much we expect our relationships to offer us permanence, stability or excitement, but most of us probably hope they will serve as a source of personal growth.

All relationships contain both intimate and non-intimate interactions, and have phases in which we want different levels of separateness and closeness. We all probably expect and experience different sorts of intimacy from relationships as couples, as extended family members, in friendship and work systems. This may change as we age. As partners in couple relationships in particular, our needs will not always coincide: we may struggle to manage different rules or beliefs about physical and emotional intimacy and communication. Over the years, we may find our hopes have been unrealistic, that we make assumptions without checking them out, be this about what the other can give or what we are being asked for. What we want from one another may change at a pace that does not fit comfortably for both: attitudes and habits can become entrenched, reducing conversations to comments of criticism or correction. Differences valued earlier can later threaten the very integrity of a relationship. Rivalries can escalate, and styles of emotional expression can come to feel unsatisfactory and require renegotiation: some couples try to exclude anger by vesting decision-making power in one person; some avoid anger by closing off areas where differences threaten, while still others use anger and conflict as growth points.

Becoming *parents* affects relationships: it can lead to increased closeness and a sense of shared responsibility, or to obstacles: children can become the forum through which couples resolve differences and difficulties, so that separation becomes a dangerous threat; alternatively, differences in attitudes to parenting can escalate to permeate all other aspects of relationships, until couple relationships cannot be viewed in isolation from child-rearing.

Just because one person is ill does not mean these issues disappear. Almost inevitably, illness introduces imbalance to relationships, altering how needs for closeness and distance are experienced and managed, impacting on the psychological well-being of individuals and couples. This can affect the issues couples feel able to discuss with one another: whether, for example, to risk burdening one another with fears about treatment methods, about increased incapacity or concerns unrelated to illness. Although patients are often told to avoid stress, paradoxically tensions mount with attempts to avoid the ill person's exposure to the stresses of real family life.

Where relationships have valued *equality* based on similarity, changes are required to reinterpret equality and redefine connectedness. Alternatively, where relationships have valued *difference* or inequality, roles partners played prior to illness may be challenged depending on who becomes ill: if the person who played the 'strong protector', rather than 'helpless victim' becomes ill, an important relational rule is challenged, influencing what it is safe to share. So, just when the emotional and spiritual comfort their relationship could provide is most needed, they may find themselves alone and shut off from one another.

Either way, physical deterioration and potential loss of the other can evoke fears of personal vulnerability, resulting in increased intimacy or attempts to distance oneself. Pre-existing levels of trust may affect couples' readiness to explore alternatives, and one or both partners may feel unable to make changes without addressing past hurts and disappointments.

Level of incapacitation determines the change required. However, we cannot just assume what this will involve, or whether partners share similar feelings about giving or receiving care. Where sexuality has been central to their intimacy and excitement, partners need to find ways of valuing other forms of physical contact and companionship. Sometimes, sexuality can be preserved with professional guidance, a guidance that recognises worries about physical exertion, that assists couples in pursuing alternative positions or forms of sexual expression.

However, where sexual intimacy has previously been fraught, illness may provide respite from disappointment in one another, allowing couples to enjoy less highly charged physical contact, like stroking and cuddling. For still others, the speech or hearing impediments which limit verbal intimacy may be what is most devastating. The loss and shame so frequently attached to this means that sensitive input is required for individual needs to be 'heard' or met.

Opportunities for intimacy are invariably affected by past patterns of privileging one partner's needs over that of the other: in any relationship, there is not one but two constructions of reality, which may or may not be similar. The fact that one person is ill, possibly close to death, can heighten differences, affecting the balance of power.

The diagnosis means that one, but not both partners, feels ill and experiences physical discomfort or pain, is dependent on the other at a practical and possibly emotional level, and has to limit paid employment with restricted access to the outside world. This can give rise to feelings of shame, guilt, relief or resentment, increasing isolation and limiting availability to one another. This is particularly pronounced where people do not look ill, but do experience fatigue and pain. Fears born out of loneliness and fatigue easily give way to despair, an altered sense of self and unwillingness to make personal demands on others. This can have an extensive impact on couples, affecting decision-making as well as sexual relationships. Helping couples formulate a narrative that confirms rather than denies what is shared and different can facilitate more realistic planning of what can be asked for or expected.

Past rules of what to share may be insufficient to cope with the emotions evoked and couples may value help in negotiating this change. Some of the issues to consider include:

- their understanding of illness and its demands;
- who or what caused the condition;
- how they can live in the presence of threatened loss;
- connections between past, present and future priorities;
- how roles of patient and carer can be managed in a way that retains mutuality in their relationship;
- what physical intimacy they can offer and receive.;
- ill partners' hopes and expectation for the future.

Addressing similarity and difference

Differences in expectations and hopes may not easily be resolved, but sharing these differences can intensify or reintroduce intimacy. Clinically, we find ourselves facing dilemmas of how to address this. To minimise difference can be pathologising, implying differences are too risky and dangerous to discuss, but focusing solely on difference can lead to polarisation, accentuating power differentials. The resolution may lie in recognising both difference and similarity. Despite the desperation to get things right, there is unlikely to be a right or a wrong way of dealing with such powerful experiences. Instead, there may be different views, views not organised by misguided or malicious intent, but by dissimilar life experiences and beliefs, by the position of being ill or healthy, being disabled or not, having had previous contact with illness or not, and being male or female. So the meaning of any setback or reprieve is unlikely to completely similar.

As professionals, we need to extend our interest in similarity and difference. In hearing the distress of one person, we need to consider what this means for the other: while one person's 'soft spot', pre-dating illness, may be fear of losing control, the other might have been afraid of assuming responsibility for others, fears relating to childhood. Despite this, they share the fear of relationships becoming dominated by power and control.

Another couple may struggle with quite different issues: one partner could be afraid of 'poisoning' their relationship with anger and frustration, while the other may feel anxious about voicing needs for fear of evoking their partner's anger, an anger so frightening it is rarely expressed. So attempts to avoid hurting one another are paradoxically isolating.

In addition to unravelling different constructions, exploring what is shared can move couples beyond polarised positions: this could include asking them how avoiding expressing anger impacts on their relationship, or how they decided this was the safest way to be. Alternatively, we could also ask whether their relationship has always been based on looking after one another, or whether they have ever had a love that allowed them different needs for space and independence. Reflecting on such questions can alter the way in which couples view one another, moving towards a frame of relationship that is not defined purely by illness. Respecting difference while recognising what is shared may enable both partners to continue to support one another for as long as is physically and emotionally feasible.

CASE EXAMPLE

James, a married man of 45, suffered a serious myocardial infarction. He was told his prognosis was unclear and that he might not have long to live. He and his wife requested a consultation as they felt his condition was tearing them apart. At the outset, the couple talked only about what the heart attack meant for James, rather than the impact it had on their relationship or Sharon. It therefore seemed important to establish what was being excluded from their narrative.

James: I feel we've moved into no man's land, we don't know how I'll be and where this will lead.
Therapist: Is it only no man's land, or is it no woman's land as well? You, Sharon, seem uncertain what the future will now hold for you too.

Later, rather than minimising or ignoring disagreement, unravelling what this meant provided a way of addressing different experiences and expectations.

James: I don't want my friends and relatives to know too much; I can't deal with their sympathy.
Sharon: That's harder for me.
Therapist: Does it seem that if fewer people know, it's not really happening?
Sharon: I think you're ashamed of your illness.
James: That's unkind. Why say that?
Sharon: I'm not trying to be cruel.
Therapist: Why do you think he might feel ashamed?
Sharon: He said yesterday he felt he was letting us down, and you did use the word ashamed!
James: I didn't.
Sharon: The pressure is on me to make sure people don't know, to keep it secret.
Therapist: It seems this makes you both very angry: could it be that as well as being angry with Sharon about telling people, you are also angry you've been ill, that it's unfair, and some of your anger towards James is about what the illness is doing to you both?
James: I am angry, but also kind of jealous of Sharon, of her health, it doesn't seem right to say.
Sharon: That irritates and upsets me, because I haven't got an answer. You're withdrawing, keeping as much distance between us as you can. [*She begins to cry*]

Sharing their fear of losing one another helped the couple confront the differences that lay ahead for them both. While talking in this way risked increasing the pain of what would be lost in the future, it helped regain some of the intimacy they feared they had lost.

How are losses balanced against potential gains?

Illness is not only about loss, but about gains. Situations arise in which previous ways of relating become redundant and unhelpful, necessitating shifts in roles and tasks. Some of these shifts may challenge gendered stereotypes. A partner's temporary or permanent inability to fulfil a role creates the opportunity for the other to experience a new side to themselves. For example, men who are ill and have an enforced time at home may come to place increased value on family relationships, and experience greater intimacy and practical involvement with their children. Some women find that a partner's illness alters their understanding of their own ability to carry out administrative or technical skills.

These changes can herald new intimacy, intimacy evoked by fears of loss and by experiencing or re-experiencing different sides to one another. During a recovery phase, after the crisis has abated, tensions may mount as partners struggle to retain this intimacy while trying to distance themselves from the illness experience. Practical constraints like resuming employment outside the home invariably affects the intensity of emotion. Each person may have a different investment in what has been given up or lost: one may be desperate to escape reminders of illness and resume their previous lifestyle, while the other hopes to retain intimacy as a 'repayment' for the distress of illness.

CASE EXAMPLE

Returning to James and Sharon, his illness had faced the couple with vulnerability in themselves and each other. This brought them closer to one another, allowing them to balance their rivalry and previous disappointment in one another with a greater warmth and nurturance. James was employed as an accountant and Sharon was largely involved in childcare. Although Sharon's understanding of relationships meant that she was a pivotal resource to her friends, their relationship was one in which value was placed on the world outside the home: technical and academic knowledge was prioritised over the more subjective understanding of relationships. As James became physically frail, however, both he and Sharon placed greater value on this subjective, relational understanding than the more 'objective' world of scientific knowledge. Sharon also assumed greater agency in James' treatment and managing the family's finances, altering their understanding of what they could receive or expect from one another.

On recovery, resuming pre-illness lifestyles posed another shift in value systems, threatening their newly acquired intimacy. James was keen to resume his pre-illness role, to assure himself he was well and alive. However, for Sharon, this meant renouncing agency and control previously unavailable to her. Anger and frustration escalated, initiating their referral. Exploring what was excluded from their conversations meant discussing:

- how they first suspected James was unwell;
- their immediate reactions to the heart attack, including what they each understood from the diagnosis;
- what had changed for them both;
- what they had discovered about one another over this time;
- the impact of those discoveries on their relationship and parenting;
- what they now wanted of one another;
- the risks of retaining more flexible boundaries in their relationship.

Their discoveries included Sharon seeing her husband develop an intimacy with their two sons, aged 2 and 4, that she had doubted could have been possible, and James seeing his wife manage their practical and financial responsibilities in a way he had never anticipated. These were complicated gains as they had evolved from the reduced availability and incapacity of the other.

Sharon felt resentful at having to carry emotional responsibility for them both, of anticipating James' feelings. Rather than assuming this statement was the only way of understanding what was happening, James was asked how he understood this. Different views emerged: James confronted Sharon with his feelings about her speaking for him, and the couple were encouraged to think what it would mean if this were to change. Their experience had changed their expectations of one another, so this pattern, evident in many male-female relationships, no longer fitted. Asking James about others' thoughts and feelings, challenged the myth of his 'emotional/relational' ignorance. Encouraging Sharon to talk about herself, rather than her partner, provided space for her to share her story too.

Over the course of therapy, James' condition continued to improve. Undoubtedly this impacted on the risks they felt able to take in therapy. As their requirements of one another changed, they became increasingly able to acknowledge what was shared and different, and to ask for what they wanted of one another.

How does practical care-giving impact on relationships?

The *imbalance* introduced by illness can unhook relationships that have become rigidly entrenched over time, or may stretch families beyond what feels tolerable. For shorter or longer periods of time, one person becomes dependent on the care of the other, with practical, financial and emotional implication for them both. For a healthy partner, guilt or embarrassment about their own health, and frustration and even anger about restrictions to their lives can make it difficult to share personal concerns, limiting access to support, and the right to needs of their own. Paradoxically, ambivalence about care-taking may increase the healthy partner's dependence on the ill partner to a greater extent than the reverse, as if the role of care-giver can come to subsume all else.

System theory describes how a *double bind* develops where people face conflicting expectations/injunctions of how to respond (Bateson, 1969). Conflicting demands are placed on a seriously ill person by their care-givers: emphasis on personal responsibility for health means that ill people are encouraged to be active in their care, to be independent rather than passive and dependent. However, when conditions deteriorate, they are expected to submit to the care of professionals and families, regardless of whether they feel blamed for failing to avert deterioration. This affects how adults allow themselves to be cared for in intimate relationships: as a parent or partner, an ill person may have an expectation of looking after others, their children, partner, or elderly parents. However, two messages have an impact on how to fulfil this expectation: one is to continue to fulfil prescribed roles, which means neglecting personal needs in the interests of others. The other is to attend to personal well-being, including resting and accepting the care of others; while 'giving in' and acknowledging the need to be looked after adds to the burden placed on others, ignoring one's own physical needs can result in physical deterioration and prove equally burdensome. In the 1990s this is complicated by a third injunction: to achieve self-actualisation and personal growth that is not solely dependant on the psychological, physical and financial care of others.

Where doctors, nurses, physiotherapists or family members have different expectations of what the ill person can do, confusion escalates. Anger about being 'chosen' to be ill can lead to the sufferers 'giving up', feeling misunderstood, refusing to maximise their physical potential or being unable to acknowledge just how unwell they feel. As physical capability cannot be isolated from emotional state, it is difficult to decide where to draw the line, when to continue with what is expected or to respond to what the body seems to say. There can be no optimal way of balancing these powerful contradictions: what feels appropriate at any one time may be less so later. While it may seem obvious that failing to respect personal physical needs can be more damaging to others, this can evoke an intolerable sense of being weak or selfish.

As government policy stresses care in the community, it is up to us as professionals to recognise the power of these contradictions, to recognise how intimate relationships impact on the readiness to accept care and medical treatment. We need to respect fears of being overwhelmed by demands of caring for a seriously ill or disabled partner, and to assess what feels manageable. This may mean placing limits on care-giving roles. While it may seem uncomfortable, acknowledging fear or even revulsion may enable different respite options to be pursued. The 'permission' of the ill person may be required to allow partners to have a life outside beyond the caring role. This may free them to retain access to the outside world, providing conversations outside illness, and helping preserve the intimacy and dignity in their relationship crucial to enabling the ill member to remain at home longer.

Partners' wishes may not coincide, requiring considerable negotiation to ensure that their differing needs can be respected. People may value detailed information and reassurance about the actual role of respite carers and nursing assistance. This may help families establish how services provided can respect the privacy of their relationship and home. Changes in the condition can mean that expectations of what is needed and available are not shared. Where a partner or family members feel overburdened, professionals can help by:

- setting up network meetings, including the couple/family, to establish long-term care plans, and explore expectations of needs and resources;
- exploring ways of increasing access to extended family members, like adult children or siblings, for help with tasks such as shopping and transport;
- relieving partners of tasks they find particularly upsetting, such a having to dress a wound, assisting in dialysis, or attending to personal hygiene.

However, illness often re-evokes painful needs in relationships where such needs have never been acknowledged or met. While some prefer to turn to adult children, others feel unresolved issues make it impossible to ask partners or adult children for anything. In a family in which the mother's incapacitation led her to approach her adult daughter for support, what was crucial was encouraging them to share some of their past hurts and disappointments before the current issues could be addressed. Having this 'special cry' together outside the sessions enabled both mother and daughter to create a narrative of their relationship that included the possibility of a more nurturant style of caring.

Drawing a family tree, a genogram, can be a way of revisiting old stories, introducing themes that had previously been left out, so that relationships can be redefined in a way that allows greater access to support within the family.

There are enormous financial implications when a primary breadwinner has to give up work to care for an ill partner or parent. As single adults, daughters in particular are often expected to put their lives on hold to care for ill parents. This is more likely when the parent lives alone, but may also occur when the illness confronts the couple with issues they cannot face together. Where this continues over prolonged periods, a family consultation can provide the context in which to re-assess expectations and explore alternatives that distribute the demands more equitably.

CASE EXAMPLE

In this family, the mother had been diagnosed with ovarian cancer. An adult daughter, Emma, was recruited back into the home to look after her mother and two much younger siblings. This allowed her father to retain his career, ensuring the financial security of the family. While this seemed helpful initially, as the mother's condition improved, the siblings began to exhibit behavioural difficulties and became increasingly reluctant to accept Emma's authority. Emma urged the family to seek consultation about her siblings. She and her parents decided the three of them should attend the initial consultation.

Here, Emma revealed her resentment of what her parents expected of her; she also felt they could not cope without her, that reducing her contribution could impede her mother's recovery or lead to a recurrence of cancer. She had given up a university course to help her family, so a shift involved not only resuming her studies, but facing what the loss of that year meant to her.

Exploring how the decision had been reached for Emma to continue to 'stand in' for her parents included exploring what alternatives were available.

- What arrangements would the parents have to make if Emma was less available?
- How might this affect the couple's relationship?
- What would have to happen for Emma to be convinced her parents could cope without her?
- What might she want from them now?

Although Emma and her parents did not agree on what was best, this conversation freed her to move out of the family home, re-register for a course and limit her availability to her family. This allowed/forced the parents to assume a different role in relation to their younger children. Moreover, it refocused issues on the couple rather than the daughter.

Not all adults are in relationships with access to someone who can take care of them. Many live alone, are divorced, widowed or reluctant to be cared for by their children. People who are in shorter-term relationships may find the illness invites greater intimacy and dependency than previously desired, possibly forma-lising relationships that had been defined in terms of distance and personal independence. This may be as true of friendships, relation-ships with extended family members and sexual partners. Although this creates a powerful opportunity for reformulating relationships, the risk is that illness becomes integral to intimacy.

How does gender impact on how care is negotiated?

Ignoring gender can pathologise differences in the reactions of men and women which are understandable if gender is taken into account.

The last 30 years have witnessed a shift in our understanding of how gender constructs our lives. Women have begun to realise that their subjective experience has been largely shaped by a culture that expects them both to be men's sexual objects and to serve as carers of others. Although less extensively, men too are beginning to question the restrictions posed by current ideas of masculinity, and the impact this has on relating to men, women and children. However, despite shifts in social attitude and employment strategies, changes to the division of household chores and positions in employment have been limited. In the health service, positions of authority remain held primarily by men rather than women, so assumptions about identity, emotional expression and appropriate care are largely informed by the views of men.

In many ways, stories of selfhood remain largely supported by traditional views of masculinity and femininity: for men, development is construed in terms of securing independence from the mother, linking masculinity with a sense of self-defined by action and control, frequently involving control over women; for women, less emphasis is placed on defining a self in opposition to mothers, but there is still an emphasis on the ability to foster and maintain interpersonal relationships. Caring roles therefore remain unevenly distributed and valued according to gender: women still tend to have primary responsibility for caring roles, while men largely retain the higher-status roles connected to financial reward and prestige outside the home. Viewing caring as the domain of women powerfully constructs how men and women understand their right to be looked after, and how caring for oneself can be integrated with caring for others.

In challenging rules about personal control, responsibility, the capacity to care for others and intimacy, illness introduces men and women to roles they may or may not be prepared for, roles that might assault their very sense of masculinity or femininity. The conflicts, contradictions and restrictions this poses may be considerable, influencing:

- *The emotional expression we allow ourselves and others*: when, or even whether, we allow ourselves to show fear, panic and sadness. As different styles of expression are valued in men and women, it can become confusing when we are confronted with feelings and expressions that do not fit expectations.

- *Adjustment to the incapacitation of illness*: constraints in communication, through speech and hearing disability, and to non-verbal communication and sexuality may mean different things to men and women.
- *How we describe and understand symptoms*: while men tend to use largely physical terms, women use emotional terms focused on the effect events have for relationships, organising assumptions of appropriate sick roles.
- *The meaning of being unable to perform tasks traditionally linked to gender identity*: even where illness is short-lived, the impact of gendered shifts may last well beyond temporary suspension of role.
- *The sort of support we provide and receive*: professionals, families and friends give emotional support to both men and women, but appear to provide instrumental support only to women.

This raises the importance of:

- ensuring men and women have clear understanding of what will be expected of them;
- providing opportunities to discuss what they find most difficult, and acknowledge the feelings aroused;
- providing a context to explore alternatives such as respite care and/or extended family involvement;
- considering who can be approached for assistance or tutoring in untried tasks.

Men and women seem to experience illness in different ways. There is evidence to suggest that psychological adjustment is better when men rather than women are ill, but men experience greater difficulty than women when their partner is ill (Ell *et al.*, 1988). Complex processes of internalisation, assimilation and socialisation of roles may account for this. Socio-cultural norms in Britain, mean that when a man is ill, his partner is expected to undertake roles previously seen to be the man's domain. As these tasks are more highly valued by society, the contradictions this poses to self-identity may be experienced as growth-inducing rather than disconfirming. This is likely to be less true of the contradictions presented to men who find themselves having to take over women's roles in families.

While many men have difficulty in acknowledging dependency, at another (more covert) level they are more accustomed to having their emotional needs met by women, so may be both readier to state demands or respect their right to receive care. When a woman is ill, she may have less clear expectations of what her partner should/could provide, even to the extent of assuming his emotional needs should subsume hers. In this instance, she may limit her own access to care, and paradoxically inhibit his care-giving in the attempt to avoid overburdening him. Research highlights this ambivalence with evidence that women increase rather than decrease time spent on household chores when ill (Hafstrom and Schram, 1984). This level of activity may be confusing, adding to men's ambivalence about their appropriate roles as carers.

CASE EXAMPLE

Melanie, aged 40, had been diagnosed with breast cancer which later spread, resulting in a paralysis of her lower legs. She contacted the clinic as she felt concerned about her daughter of 13 and two sons, aged 6 and 8. In an initial session with her and her partner, Phillip, they shared their struggle to negotiate the shifts in responsibility the illness had initiated. Prior to the illness, although they both worked outside the home, she as a teacher and he as a scientist, primary responsibility for childcare lay with Melanie. She discussed her fears for the children as if these concerns were hers alone. As most of their extended family lived in Ireland, she felt isolated and worried about how Phillip would cope with their children, particularly their daughter's adolescence.

Melanie: I thought carefully about being a parent, read things and that was very helpful for me. So I'm really worried now, how harmful I might be to the children. I know I might die and I don't know what will happen.

Therapist: I wonder how that fits with your ideas about coming here today, Phillip?

Philip: I'm here because you suggested seeing us both. I followed Melanie.

Therapist: What are your own thoughts of what it's like for your children?

Philip: I suppose my fear about Melanie dying is more personal, what I'll do with the kids, not making our daughter into a little mummy. I waver between thinking Melanie will survive six months or ten years, and any time in between. It's frightening. Sometimes I think she'll live and then I'll have to live with that! (*They both laugh*) I try not to look at things until they happen, are forced on me.

Therapist: So you have different styles of thinking about this. I don't know if that's something to do with differences in how men and women manage things. I wonder, Melanie, how does Phillip's not looking ahead help you at this time?

Rather than assuming talking about the future is the best way to face the illness, gender provides a lens that is not about right and wrong for considering difference. Subsequent to the diagnosis, they had become preoccupied with different issues: Phillip had become the 'expert' on physiological aspects of the condition, and Melanie on the emotional impact this might have on children. This was evident in how they discussed Melanie's chances of survival: he in terms of statistical probability and she in terms of emotional consequences.

Issues about control and authority, a source of contention throughout their relationship, were exacerbated now Melanie was ill.

Melanie: I've always tended to plan and have the ideas, and you go along. It's hard to think about not being there for the children, not being in control. That's part of what it would mean for me if I die.
Therapist: It sounds very painful. Have you discussed this together before?
Melanie: Well, we've fought about it before, and still do. It's been a sort of catch 22: I wanted Phil to take on more, but wouldn't give up until he did.
Therapist: What do you feel has to happen for things to change now?
Phillip: More trust. I'd have to feel in control to do more.
Therapist: How would that be different for your children?
Philip: It's already starting; rather than relying on Melanie, I'm reacting more myself.
Therapist: You've obviously given this a good deal of thought, but it's been hard to achieve. How do you understand that?

Although Phillip had assumed more responsibility within their home since Melanie had been ill, he felt undermined by her and ambivalent about his role. He felt unsure and untrained as a man to do what she had managed so well, and uncomfortable about succeeding in an area powerfully identified with her sense of herself as woman. Placing her expertise on a pedestal meant that rather than using her as a resource, he felt he needed to prove he could cope. It also meant Melanie could not focus on what she herself wanted. Rather than which ideas on child-rearing were best, work focused on how being a man and a woman influenced their ideas. Phillip raised his anxiety about the anger he sometimes felt towards their children. Melanie responded with the wisdom she had gained from talking to other women, that most parents felt that way at times. This allowed them to think of how Phillip could be 'tutored' by his wife in a way that freed him to rely on his own ideas. As they were worried about his managing their daughter's menarche and emergent sexuality, access to other women 'tutors' in their extended family was explored.

Therapist: How does this relate to what your own parents had to face?

Ideas about a gendered self are influenced not only by cultural constructs, but by relationships within our families of origin. Melanie's view of her mother as ineffective in the face of an overbearing father, and Phillip's memory of his father appearing helpless and distancing himself during crises, constructed how they understood relationships. They were determined to do things differently in their relationship with one another, but had been provided with role models that were difficult to erase. This was heightened by the challenge to control the illness presented. Phillip felt that having to stand in for his father at those times had left him with a selfish 'survival' streak. Asking how what he had learned through this might help him think about his children's needs placed a less damning frame on his experience.

As indicated earlier, the physical and emotional care of someone who is ill can alter each person's sense of self, personal vulnerability, and expectations of adult relationships. Each symptom change signifies a potential shift in roles and relationships, requiring delicate negotiation to ensure that the ill person is not prematurely robbed of self-identity, yet frees the partner to assume the task at hand. Some role changes may be central to each person's gendered identity: for a woman and mother, her male partner having to provide emotional care to her daughter or son alters her sense of herself as a woman; for a man and father, a partner taking on tasks that defined his masculinity as head of the household renders the shift in roles more difficult for them both. On recovery, it may feel important to ensure the ill person reassumes these tasks, to enable him or her to reconnect with their pre-illness identity. But to do so means their partner risks renouncing her greater sense of agency and control (for women), or changing his pattern of relating to their children (for men).

Whilst these examples have focused on slightly younger couples, these issues are equally applicable to older couples for whom changes in role, experiences of incontinence or a mastectomy may present a tremendous challenge to the gendered identity of both partners. Bringing thoughts about gender overtly into discussions provides an alternative lens through which to explore relationships, potentially enhancing control in situations people feel they can do little to change. It may therefore be useful to ask:

- How does being a man or woman influence your response to illness?
- What do you feel least prepared for?
- What/who could help your preparation?
- What do you think you might learn from trying these new roles?

Addressing stigma in illness

A diagnosis of illness is not an isolated event. The care needed during an illness may lead to a more public acknowledgement of relationships that had been kept secret or private: couples may have delayed telling parents about mixed race or mixed religion relationships, and continuing prejudice about homosexuality means that many gay and lesbian relationships are kept secret from family members. Where an illness brings a person's current life in contact with their family of origin for the first time, reactions may relate as much to the disclosure of the relationship as to the disease itself. Sometimes, parents and adult siblings respond to such disclosures by attempting to exclude the ill person's current partner.

While my own clinical work has not focused on AIDS cases, the issues seem too important to exclude here. Despite attempts to shift public attitudes, current representations of AIDS are dominated by blame, punishment and moral retribution. This means that people with AIDS have to balance the potential consequences of disclosure with their need for support in the face of growing physical discomfort. Although there are indications that progression from HIV-positive status to full blown AIDS is not as rapid as previously assumed, the disease is still seen as a death sentence, compounding feelings aroused by a diagnosis.

Paradoxically, terminal phases of the disease present the greatest opportunities for flexibility: the urgency of time can provide the impetus to create a meaningful shift in relationships, enabling expectations of one another to be viewed differently. Observing the care partners provide for one another can free other family members to come to terms with their children's or siblings' life choices, enabling them to create a narrative of their lives that has a more positive meaning (Walker, 1991).

However, for AIDS and other sexually transmitted diseases the threat of infecting one's partner can render it more difficult to discuss emotions, such as feelings of shame, guilt and despair. Sadly, AIDS does not end with death: the loss, grief and anger of witnessing a loved one suffering can become mixed with rage about possible infection and contamination. This can affect practical aspects of coping, like sexual practice, or remaining vigilant for the physical changes which could signify a deterioration and the need for further treatment. As AIDS can isolate individuals and families from community support, self-help organisations provide an invaluable alternative community for those who are ill and their carers, helping safeguard relationships from prejudice.

With all families facing stigma in this way, it may require someone outside the relationship, a professional or friend, to hear about confusion and pain, and help evolve a narrative that extends beyond one of destruction.

How can a sense of dignity and quality of life be retained?

There is no guarantee the person diagnosed with a life-threatening condition will be the first to die. Focusing exclusively on illness and treatment may be appropriate at crisis stages but, when retained for prolonged periods, relationships can become subsumed by illness, leading to feelings of resentment and guilt that are difficult to manage. So finding ways of avoiding skewing all interactions on the basis of illness are crucial to preserving intimacy and dignity.

Externalising the condition, even finding a special word for it, emphasises that someone is not only a cancer, AIDS or multiple sclerosis victim, but a full-blooded, physical and emotional being. Although medical equipment may be essential to maintaining the quality of life of an ill person, concrete limits, like creating a space where such equipment, pills and conversations about illness are banned, can emphasise that there are other aspects to life (Rolland, 1994). While healthy partners or family members need to spend time outside, continuing to invite friends home also extends the possibility of relationships having an identity beyond illness.

Modern medicine means partners or family members may face difficult decisions about respecting a terminally ill person's dignity and wishes. This is particularly difficult where strongly held wishes conflict with the recommendations of the medical team or other family members, or where they have not been stated sufficiently formally to be clear to all. This may escalate in future years: medical practitioners are predicting advances that will necessitate patients and their families becoming increasingly involved in decisions about treatment. Where feasible, asking family members to put themselves in the place of (or talk as if they were) the other, may enable different perspectives to emerge. As with all clinical work, our role is to help families find ways of resolving differences themselves, within the confines of the legal structure, rather than imposing our prejudices and expectations.

A partner's illness may elicit tremendous fears about personal vulnerability, or strike just when the couple were planning to separate. While crises can evoke an intimacy that was previously missing, this is not always so, and partners may fear being trapped into staying in a situation that feels frighteningly restrictive or destructive. Access to non-judgemental consultation, in which the feelings of rage, guilt and shame can be acknowledged, may be crucial in assisting couples to face these important, painful personal decisions. For some, the only way of continuing to support one another is by achieving greater distance between them. Some decide to separate formally, while others find a way of living more separately within their shared home.

Faced with a partner's physical deterioration and the loss of a secure future together, flight from intimacy may be the only recourse the healthy partner has in managing their devastating loss. Where this flight has included extra-marital affairs, couples may feel more ambivalent about re-establishing closeness. However, where there is sufficient trust, they may want to try reintroducing intimacy into their relationship: returning to thinking about what had attracted them to one another and how this relates to their present life may be important in this process. Ambivalence is probably most pronounced where the condition has led to gross personality and cognitive changes, so that while physically present, the person is emotionally and cognitively absent.

Not all couples and family members are equally ready to confront the powerful emotions aroused by illness and may find ways of dissuading one another from expressing feelings: there may be fears of hastening the course of illness or having too little time to resolve old hurts and disappointments. There may be times when professionals, too, struggle to face the issues raised, influencing what can or cannot be said. At these times, access to consultation is important. Despite the urgency of the possibility of death, it is important that work proceeds at a pace that feels safe, a pace dictated by professional and family alike. Decisions about what is safe to share rest with the family and influences the timing and pacing of individual or joint sessions. Creating space for each person to gain some understanding of their own response can free them to redefine their connectedness, and retain agency, competence and integrity.

Having emphasised the potential growth an illness can initiate, it would be inappropriate to minimise the fear, physical disgust and humiliation that can disempower men and women as they struggle to manage pain, fatigue, disfigurement or socially unacceptable levels of incontinence. It is therefore essential we all examine what we can do in our different contexts to empower the people we meet in our work. This includes ensuring our own authority does not unwittingly undermine the dignity of families, prioritising the emotional and spiritual costs of treatment; and ensuring people have time to digest scientifically-based decisions, be this about care packages or treatment options. In a climate of diminishing public resources, it may be up to us to remain vigilant about whether services match the needs families experience.

Conclusions

Ill adults face the difficult issue of balancing appropriate personal health behaviour with attending to the needs of other family members. Each family and/or couple will seek to find ways of resolving this that best fits with their hopes and expectations. Differing needs for intimacy, distance and separation have to be negotiated with ongoing demands for giving and receiving care for oneself and others. Care is inevitably a reciprocal systemic process. This negotiation depends not only on those recognised as carers, but on the support and *care* the ill person is able to provide too.

Although illness in one adult affects all family members, a tremendous imbalance of power is introduced when only one member enters a world organised by pain, discomfort or disfigurement and others remain physically able to pursue their lives. The stage of life at which an illness strikes, the course of the condition and the support available influence how families negotiate this. This will influence whether their illness narratives encompass the experience of not one but all family members, safeguarding an identity not totally consumed by illness.

We can all play an important role in listening to the stories told by the people we encounter, and considering how aspects of their stories that are not easily shared can be incorporated. Whether working with individuals, couples, family members or intervening in the wider network, like medical and social service systems, we need ensure our encounters strive to preserve that sense of personal respect and dignity intrinsic to family well-being.

Summary

1. The age and life stage at which illness strikes affects both the demands placed on family members, and impacts on the range of decisions presented, like whether to have children.

2. Research, largely informed by views of outsiders, clinicians and scientists, has highlighted the impact a serious illness can have on adult relationships. More recently, there has been a move towards focusing on the families' own stories, illustrating strategies used in coping with and managing illness, and the unique *gains* and *losses* illness may pose for relationships.

3. Clinical work has focused on these *illness narratives*, exploring ways of incorporating options currently excluded from stories, like the story of the healthy partner, how illness has affected relationships, gendered identity and self-concept.

4. This enables us to consider how couples face the *difference* or *imbalance* imposed by demands for care-taking when a partner becomes ill and disabled. Attempts to *deny* difference unwittingly *escalate* problems as it implies difference is too dangerous to discuss; alternatively too great a focus on difference can lead to unhelpful *polarisation* and *isolation*.

5. Either choice can impact on how *intimacy* is retained, and practical guidance about retaining a life less dictated by illness can prove useful. Misguided attempts to be helpful can result in the ill person being prematurely excused from family tasks or decisions, reducing their scope for a life less circumscribed by illness.

6. Gender constructs our self-identity and understanding of the meaning of care, influencing decisions about providing and receiving care.

7. The balance of potential gains and losses may be more precarious when the condition leads to disclosing a relationship that has been kept *secret*, or when the condition carries a particular *stigma*, as with AIDS.

8. Here as elsewhere, it is important to respect that there may be *limits on what people feel they can share*.

9. Our professional role lies in providing space for families to consider the impact of the illness and its treatment on the *dignity* and *quality of their lives*, so members can reach informed decisions they feel comfortable with.

8

PERSONAL AND PRACTICAL ISSUES
FOR PROFESSIONALS

This chapter refocuses attention on professionals working with illness. Whilst the first chapter discussed our position in the health system, this chapter concentrates on the personal implications of our work.

CASE EXAMPLE

Returning to a case discussed earlier (Chapter 5) Daniel, a 5-year-old boy, and his 32-year-old mother, Jane, were referred to the child and family outpatient clinic by their GP who was concerned about their response to Jane's breast cancer. He had been alerted by Daniel's teacher, who felt his behaviour in class, variable concentration, aggressive outbursts and unusual facial mannerisms were signs of distress. Despite considerable treatment, a mastectomy, chemotherapy and radiotherapy, the cancer had spread and it appeared unlikely she would survive the year. Jane herself had been looked after by her grandmother in Trinidad when a child, after being abandoned by her parents. She felt she had been similarly abandoned in Britain by Daniel's father, a year after his birth.

The mother and son were seen by myself, with a colleague, Barbara Dale, behind the screen. At our initial meeting, I tried to ascertain from them why they had come. From then, Jane began to swamp me with details about her son's early development, her treatment and illness. Whenever I tried to intervene, to build on her son's attempts to distract her and help him make sense of what was happening both inside and outside the room, she returned to her story. It seemed she was unable to think about her son without being sure I had heard and borne witness to each frightening aspect of their story.

As the session progressed, I found myself distracted, becoming irritated and bored. I felt I was struggling to hold on to my own sense of coherence; so much so, that when Daniel drew a picture of his mother with a big hole just where her mastectomy was, and she said 'That's not right, I have not got a hole there', I could not respond to her and joined my colleague for consultation. Only on re-entering the room was I able to return to the drawing, to ask Jane what she thought Daniel had been trying to say or show.

On reflection, I realise I was made to experience some of what the mother was facing. I felt swamped with uncontained and uncontainable information, embarrassed and uncomfortable with what this 5-year-old was being exposed to, yet unable to protect him from what I saw as an assault. I felt unable to make things feel better, to feel an effective professional. I can now appreciate how my unsuccessful attempts to create what I thought was order in the room mirrored their frustrated attempts to control what seemed uncontrollable: her disease, abandonment and the likelihood of Daniel experiencing what she herself had faced, a mother who leaves and does not return.

There are many differences between that woman and me: our physical health, race, culture, the parenting we received, educational opportunities and socio-economic circumstances. Yet like her, I am a woman, a mother and an immigrant. At one level, my view that swamping Daniel with information would raise anxiety and confusion in his mind was a valid concern. However, my anger towards her for being unable, or as I saw it, unwilling to recognise his needs related not only to what they were sharing with me, but to my own identification with the family.

I have used this example to illustrate how failing to recognise and attend to the personal implications of work with illness can restrict our capacity to listen, inhibiting the flexibility of the people we meet at a time of major flux. Understanding personal reactions to people facing life-threatening conditions or inexplicable symptoms labelled psychosomatic raises key dilemmas:

- *Maintaining emotional distance*: how to find appropriate closeness or distance from illness.
- *Facing personal limitations and vulnerabilities*: how to understand and address the powerful feelings this work may evoke in ourselves.

- *Reducing stress levels:* how to understand and alleviate the high levels of stress and burn out reported amongst health professionals.
- *Understanding gender constructs:* how to address the challenge physical illness presents to gendered constructions of care-giving and receiving.
- *Reconising the interactional nature of health care:* how to integrate the awareness that as professionals and families, our experience is inevitably a co-construction: just as our beliefs, assumptions and anxieties about health influence the family's responses, so our behaviour may reflect what is happening for the family.
- *Managing personal and professional boundaries:* how to balance the anxieties aroused with sufficient support, both at work and home.

It is vital that we confront these issues, particularly in our changing health-care system where moves towards specialisation, privatisation, the push for cost cutting and increasing technological developments are altering definitions of health care. The traditional healing skills of understanding, recognising distress and eliciting illness narratives are in danger of being devalued, reframing ideas about professional identity and competence, with enormous implications for patient care.

What does appropriate emotional distance mean?

In facing illness, family members often struggle to give one another the space they want, while satisfying differing and fluctuating needs for communication, separateness and intimacy. Professionals also struggle with debates around distance, how to find the appropriate level of closeness or distance from illness and those who are ill. While we probably broadly agree on the requirements of professional relationships, such as setting boundaries and avoiding forms of self-disclosure and affection that could be misinterpreted, we agree less what this actually means for relationships with colleagues, ill people and their families. Theoretical views vary enormously, undoubtedly influenced by personal and professional fears, fantasies and understanding of the processes of infection and contamination. Calls to pay greater respect to the patient's views are accompanied by reminders of the practical constraints of time, warnings of the risk of getting too close, and not being able to contain the feelings aroused in both patient and professional. Just as family members often distance themselves from someone who is dying for protection, professional attempts to 'cut off', or depersonalise an ill person, may be ways of protecting ourselves from our own pain and vulnerability.

The issues are by no means simple: what may be comfortable for professionals is not always in the best interests of patient care. Interventions like splitting nurses' duties and moving them from ward to ward, ritualised routines and adopting a detached attitude, may provide protection against opposing feelings of pity, compassion, hatred and revulsion (Menzies Lyth, 1957). However, these actions are often experienced as dehumanising, unhelpful and punitive by patients.

For medical professionals, the body is the site of care. In physically handling the body, maintaining distance may feel essential, a way of coping with inflicting pain in treatment: indeed, dehumanisation is common in perpetrating violence. However, few of us need reminding that the body is more than an object of clinical attention, but belongs to someone who may be able to speak, make eye contact, cry or argue at the time of interaction. Often, patients tell anecdotes about themselves during consultations to re-insert themselves into an impersonal, distancing situation.

These relationships are essentially social interactions, with a history that has established patterns of behaviour between medical professionals and patients. So rules of relating are not fixed: they are open to different interpretations and can change.

The debate is not confined to medical personnel. In other contexts, many of us will have worked with vulnerabilities and disorders we or our families have been spared. Here, however, retaining an attitude of 'we/they' is both indefensible and impossible as this work heightens our awareness of mortality and vulnerability (Rolland, 1994). Invariably, we are helping people with issues that affect our own lives and families. The 'rules' we use to guide our behaviour, like decisions about asking intrusive questions, may relate as much to what we ourselves, rather than the families, can tolerate.

Balint (1957) explored how relationships between doctor and patient can become strained, unhappy and even unpleasant as a result of attempts to be impersonal, limiting the possibility of hearing real pain. He suggested this can lead to non-compliance, ineffective use of resources, overutilisation of medical services with 'doctor shopping', fears of litigation and burn out. In the interests of both professional and patient's well-being, and in defiance of a training to intervene actively, he encouraged GPs to reflect, to concentrate on emotions, and risk an intimate embrace with patients.

In teams or individually, when we are concerned about our emotional distance from the work, it is useful to consider:

- What are the connections and differences between this person/ family and myself?
- How does this relate to distance I place between myself and this person/family?
- How does my behaviour fit with what is expected on the unit?

Rather than denying connections, confronting what we do and do not share enables us to recognise which issues reflect the families' concerns or belong with us. This can help us find a distance that feels respectful to ourselves and others, avoiding swamping others with our own fears and fantasies.

Facing personal limitations and vulnerabilities

Modern medicine wins many battles, but inevitably loses the final battle: we all die. Regardless of our role in the health system, we have to face the fact that, despite the best efforts of the patient, family and ourselves, people die. In many situations there is no one correct choice of treatment. The struggle to tolerate this ambiguity can lead to patients being overtreated, undertreated or even relatively abandoned. Although the hospice movement has helped to shift goals of treatment from cure to care, people who do not get better still threaten our personal and professional integrity. Identifying with those who undergo painful or mutilating experiences can exacerbate these sentiments, leaving us feeling ashamed and failures.

While facing personal limitations and vulnerability is often viewed as causing burn out, what is rarely considered is the distress caused by blocking out emotions. Far from leaving us less able to work effectively, accessing personal feelings enables us to listen more carefully and express greater empathy. Indeed, feedback suggests that what is most valued by ill patient and their families is professionals' ability to empathise and even be self-critical.

However, these ideas are not widely held. Most of us are still taught the value of hiding feelings, rather than being encouraged to reflect on when and how much to share before it becomes burdensome for others, or how acknowledging personal feelings enables others to accept painful or unacceptable feelings. Without this, we can be left assuming our responses are pathological or abnormal.

Essentially, we need to reconsider the psychological cost of current practice, to re-assess whether it is helpful or actually harmful. This means thinking creatively about what we bring to our work, without dispensing entirely with the notion of professional distance. There can be no single answer: solutions to managing distance need to include having to deal with transitory relationships, saying good-bye to many people we have come to know in an intimate, albeit professional, context. Training may help us develop our communication skills, so we find a way of moving in and out of relationships that feels respectful and enhances rather than negates our sense of self-worth. However, this can only be achieved with sufficient structures for support: change requires considering what this would mean for the whole system, for professionals, patients and families.

Individual solutions may need to address our belief systems too: like the families we meet, we probably need more realistic attitudes to illness, to the limits of our personal responsibility and omnipotence.

How does emotional vulnerability relate to our family of origin?

Multi-generational histories of unresolved loss, blame, shame or guilt influence the meaning we attribute to what we hear, and the meanings we participate in developing. Witnessing my younger brother's illness as a child, and more recently my parents' illnesses has heightened my awareness of how experiences with actual and feared loss influence our ability to tolerate fear, pain, expressions of anger, depression and even manic behaviour in others. These experiences may sensitise us to particular issues, or limit our clinical effectiveness, leading us to eulogise or denigrate someone struggling with physical symptoms. As many of us choose to work in areas that relate to our personal experience, we are likely to meet situations that reflect these personal histories, returning us to past hurts or overpowering emotions. While we may need the reassurance we are being helpful, this is rarely available. Often, I and my colleagues find ourselves leaving a session and engaging in activities that are a statement of health, be it laughing or physical exercise, to assert our difference and distance ourselves from identification.

Each of us is likely to meet a family which acts as a trigger, re-evoking automatic reactions. Recognising the roles we played as children may avoid us unwittingly re-suming the roles we know too well: the rescuer, aggressor, or scapegoat. Age, position in the family and gender can lead us to identify more closely, intensifying vulnerability. Less concrete factors, like nervous habits or a tendency to joke when afraid, may remind us of parents or siblings, restricting our readiness to empathise with the person we are addressing, be this someone who experiences physical symptoms but is told they are not real, or parents who are angry a loved child is dying.

CASE EXAMPLE

Lan was a rather isolated 37-year-old Chinese single mother with a history of alcohol abuse. She was referred to the clinic by her oncologist, who was anxious about her response to deteriorating cancer, her non-compliance with treatment, and the impact this was having on her 10- and 6-year-old daughters.

Lan asked to come alone initially. She shared her difficulty in deciding who would look after her daughters and what an awful mother she had been to them. On hearing her story, I was aware how disempowered she felt. This did not seem to reflect her bravery as a mother, how she had managed to ensure her children were cared for even when drinking, and how, despite fears about her mothering, she could risk seeing a professional who could confirm her worst fears.

I began asking how she found the courage to come to the unit, and how she had arranged for her daughters' care when she was unavailable. While Lan seemed fleetingly valued by these questions, she became irritated and detached as I pursued this line. Noting her reaction, I became aware that what I was pursuing related to my own experiences, to what it meant to me to hear another woman's sense of herself as a bad mother, to hear the pain and personal responsibility of having failed another. While recognising her courage became important later in the work, initially she wanted her failure to be heard.

Genograms or *family trees* are a useful way of uncovering and understanding how themes pertinent to this work are passed down through generations: intergenerational experiences of loss, damage, vulnerability, personal blame and strength influence what we can hear or know, and how we respond to experiences that do not fit with our expectations. We may, for example, discover how we use current experiences to right our past wrongs or hurts, what 'scripts' we are attempting to correct, or how we are forcing the present to replicate the past. When stuck and unable to think effectively, focusing on connections between interactions with the patient/ family and our family of origin can free us to think more creatively.

What contributes to stress amongst health professionals?

Growing recognition of the burn out rate of working with seriously ill people has emphasised the importance of understanding the role of stress in the maintenance and onset of physical and psychological distress. Researchers largely differentiate between 'stress', factors in the external environment, and 'strain', the impact of this stress on individuals. This is however, rather simplistic. Stress is not inevitably a source of strain: many of us feel operating at relatively high levels of external stress is intrinsic to our self-esteem, personal and professional satisfaction. We can also feel considerable strain without being under external stress: often, our own unattainable standards or goals lead to guilt, low self-esteem and strain. Contexts unrelated to illness have their own dynamics and it is meaningless to argue one profession is more stressful than another. However, factors contributing to stress in health-care systems appear to be:

- seeing oneself as hurting when trained to help;
- the powerlessness evoked in seeing people deteriorate and die, when trained to cure;
- face-to-face contact with people in pain, who may feel distressed or out of control;
- having to cope with constant change, endlessly saying good-bye;
- the lack of feedback from patients, families and colleagues in a context of ongoing uncertainty;
- the costliness of mistakes in judgement, which can lead to death, permanent damage and even litigation;
- the possibility of infection with conditions like hepatitis and AIDS;
- the structural organisation in which tasks are carried out.

The profound assumptions underlying our work are often contradictory. These vary somewhat according to our different professions, position in the hierarchy and prevailing beliefs of the unit, contradictions such as needing:

- to be present and intimate, yet respect patients' personal autonomy and boundaries;
- to be financially productive, conscious of cost cutting, yet avoid malpractice;
- to be efficient with a fast turnover, while taking time to attend to detail;
- to be accurate, provide clarity and efficiency in a context where clarity does usually exist;
- to respect authority while retaining sufficient autonomy to respond to emergencies.

However, relationships with ill people are also deeply fulfilling, an important source of self-worth and job satisfaction. Indeed, our choice of career may be based on a deep need to help others in pain. But, our support and expectations of professional-patient interactions determine whether these relationships become stressful or immensely satisfying.

How do context and role contribute to stress?

Attempts have been made to understand how training, roles, positions within the hierarchy, type of illness, structure of unit and the actual treatment delivered impact on physical and emotional stress (see Slaby and Glicksman, 1986; Payne, 1987; Firth-Cozens, 1992, for extended analysis). Overload, fatigue, professional status and financial reward are amongst the major factors which emerge. In addition, the amount of time we spend with patients and families, the stigma of the disease treated, the potential risk to life, and the disfiguring or intrusive nature of treatment profoundly influence how we and others value our contributions. Some of us, like psychologists and psychotherapists, may worry about our psychological intrusion, that we may increase rather than take away pain by encouraging patients or staff to face vulnerability and loss. For medical colleagues, what may be difficult to bear is inflicting physical pain or damage when aiming to cure.

Power differences embedded in responsibility and status are inevitably open to abuse. On inpatient wards, doctors have the greatest overt control with primary responsibility for admissions, treatment and referral, while the nurses' roles of providing support, care and containment are relatively unacknowledged and devalued, as reflected in salaries. Since positions of authority are still largely occupied by men, this mirrors the power balance dominant in society.

Assumptions of responsibilities do not always coincide with what happens in reality and there may be some crucial mismatch of expectations: for example, physicians are expected to provide emotionally charged information and then help people assimilate what this means. However, the latter is often left to those who cannot easily escape, to nurses and junior staff. Rather than acknowledging this work with support, less highly paid and junior staff fulfil these roles in an unrecognised, undervalued manner. This affects interactions with patients and colleagues, influencing later vocational choices.

The condition treated determines our exposure to potentially distressing experiences. Oncologists frequently face people who may die. Many report that breaking news of an initial diagnosis is easier than telling about subsequent relapses. Age seems to affect the difficulty of breaking bad news: telling children and the elderly is often easier than telling younger adults, who are less accepting and ask uncomfortable questions. So what may be most painful here is managing confrontation. While some report that facing their finiteness openly facilitates personal closeness, others experience this as harmful, both personally and professionally. Cardiologists and general surgeons report that the invasive and life-threatening nature of their work is most difficult to bear: surgery is often performed on people not yet experiencing discomfort, increasing the scope to view oneself as destructive, to identify with the mutilation of surgery. Many find their only option is to cut themselves off emotionally, to distance themselves from the patients at hand.

The fit between personal expectations and those of the unit seems extremely important. For example, on joining a renal unit, professionals trained to treat acutely ill people often feel unprepared to work with chronic conditions, where patients face long-term dependency on dialysis, feel frustrated about stringent dietary restrictions, and can become hostile to the services offered. Newcomers easily feel threatened by patients who are more expert on their condition than trained staff.

The dynamics of delegating responsibility to families in renal units carries its own dilemmas. With processes like ambulatory dialysis, where family members are trained to perform complex procedures at home, there are often worries about how effective their training has been. Infection or leaking can result in a deterioration of the condition. When problems arise, professionals have to manage opposing feelings of personal responsibility with anger about possible carelessness, while helping families face and contain their anger and disappointment. This can be equally complex with transplants: long-term involvement with chronic patients means that, in the event of a kidney rejection, professionals have to support angry and grieving families while facing their own disappointment and guilt.

Some units have introduced structural changes aimed at alleviating stress, like shift work, switching nurses between medical and surgical wards. While altering roles and the severity of conditions presented may help, reducing continuity of care may evoke feelings of abandonment in both patients and professionals. Hence these attempts can affect the establishment of relationships with patients, impacting on professional satisfaction. Emergency units frequently comprise a changing population of staff and patients. Variability seems to reduce the burden of responsibility, enhancing the capacity to manage repeated trauma, but limits informal access to support from colleagues. While recognising that stress can relate to context rather than inherent personal 'weakness' is crucial, the restructuring of services needs to be planned with a deep understanding of job satisfaction.

How can this be addressed in clinical practice and training?

Broadly speaking, stress levels can be altered by changing the context, or how we deal with situations. Such changes may challenge central beliefs about illness, selection, training and current practice. Current selection, particularly of medical students, is based primarily on academic ability. While high levels of cognitive understanding are important to training and clinical work, the ability to access complex knowledge relies not only on intellectual ability, but on the capacity to manage emotions in a highly charged environment. Some people manage this by 'cutting off', but this does not always work, resulting in considerable psychological disturbance (Hale and Hudson, 1992). Greater emphasis needs to be placed on the emotional management of stressful life events. This does not mean excluding candidates who have suffered major loss and trauma, but assessing how these experiences have been assimilated and integrated: for example, exploring how strengths and vulnerabilities influence the capacity to hear another's pain and operate under stress.

We cannot, however, address selection and training without considering our roles as qualified professionals. As trained professionals, we all act as mentors and role models, both in what is overtly taught and how we are seen to operate. Working with vulnerability in a context of ongoing emergency can leave us all feeling overwhelmed, inadequate and guilty. Where we are unable or unwilling to acknowledge our vulnerability, and go home when we feel ill, or convey a message that time off is a luxury rather than a right, we model something that speaks far louder than lectures on stress management. Realistic space for rest and pleasure can reduce the pressure we face. We need to humanise our professional development and training programmes, by placing greater emphasis on dealing with stress, be this with relaxation or counselling.

Integrating more constructive feedback than is currently available could further alleviate the stress of uncertainty, enabling us all to develop a more coherent sense of ourselves as effective professionals (Huebner, Royner and Morrell, 1981; Hale and Hudson, 1992).

Some programmes are trying to reintroduce 'I', to help professionals gain greater understanding of experience of illness. This has evolved from recognising the tendency to blame patients when treatment does not work, or to distance ourselves from people with trigger conditions like AIDS. Students have been encouraged to record patients' stories in the first person, as if they themselves had AIDS. Reducing emotional distance in this way has altered investment in patients' future and the outcome of medical care (Marshall and O'Keefe, 1995).

Consultation groups can be used to understand our reactions to patients and work systems. Rather than giving advice, these groups allow us to reflect on relationships with patients and colleagues. Including this thinking in various clinical meetings, like ward rounds and case discussions, can add tremendous depth to our clinical work and team building (Keith et al., 1993).

So too can the opportunity to reflect on how to talk about relatively taboo subjects. We are often required to talk about death or sexual practices, but rarely helped to address this openly, or to consider what such discussions mean for patient-professional relationships. Only in facing our personal reactions to these issues and thinking concretely of how we use this can we help families face what lies ahead.

Throughout this book, I have alluded to 'fit': between professionals and families, and between professionals and our work contexts. It would be irresponsible to encourage anyone to pursue behaviour that could leave us less supported at work, or affect prospects of promotion. Therefore, attempts to explore alternative needs to evolve out of conversations with staff at all levels of seniority: where initiatives are based on a co-evolution of ideas, the possibility of maintaining change is far greater.

How does this relate to gender?

As outlined earlier, gender restricts access to money, power and high status in our society, with a subtle yet powerful influence on language and thinking (Goldner, 1985; Gilligan, 1988; Burck and Speed, 1995). While the number of women entering medical trainings has increased (Kaufman Cartwright, 1987), positions of power in the British health system are largely held by men, influencing promotion prospects and relationships as colleagues.

However, the issues do not only centre on power. Gender impacts on attitudes to care, and beliefs about relating to others in distress. Disregarding this can lead to pathologising reactions to illness in both professionals and patients/families, reactions that could otherwise be viewed as normal. As professionals, we may feel uncomfortable when attitudes at work are at odds with our gendered values. Such gendered differences in the goals, values and assumptions of appropriate behaviour can lead to conflict between the providers of health care and patients, particularly women.

Unlike most professions, medicine combines the exercise of power and high status with intimate care, presenting us with two very different sources of vulnerability: the danger that intimacy could cloud our objectivity and overcome professional restraints, or that technical knowledge and skill could create distance in relationships with people who are ill, limiting access to emotional support (Gilligan, 1988). As technological knowledge still tends to be more firmly associated with men, and emotional or relational knowledge with women, retaining this duality presents us with quite different challenges, no doubt influenced by the 'fit' between personal beliefs and those of the work context.

It has been argued that women bring an alternative perspective to health care, with suggestions that women form more egalitarian relationships with patients, spend more time with patients, display higher levels of empathy and respect for children than male colleagues, and manage relationships with somatising patients in different ways from men (Kaufman Cartwright, 1987).

In a system where overt power is still more likely to be held by men, constructs based on masculine models largely dominate health care. Female doctors still face external prejudice, a relative dearth of role models, and often struggle to combine professional roles with that of homemaker, parent or wife. While some resolve this by choosing not to marry or have children, satisfying nurturing needs through patient care means continually letting go of people cared for intimately.

There has been considerable change in the gender balance of students entering medical professions. The next step is to ensure that positions of authority are less stratified in terms of gender. The effect of this remains to be seen, but there are hopes this could initiate new patterns of communication with patients and families, different ways of pacing work and relaxation, and an increased commitment to integrating work with family life, including child-rearing.

However, to ensure health-care institutions respect the participation of both men and women, we cannot merely replace one value system with another: currently male nurses feel their capacity to provide intimate care is undervalued (Zimmerman, 1995). We could argue that prevailing constructs make it more difficult, for example, for fathers to engage actively in caring for children: staff often complain 'I never see fathers.' This may be because practical constraints or personal fears make it difficult to participate in this care. But we also need to ensure that fathers are not unwittingly kept out of treatment through assumptions about their capacity to nurture an ill child, and that we do not limit our commitment to securing their participation.

As gendered constructs influence views on dealing with stress and professional competence, it may be useful to consider:

- How does gender influence decisions about physical and emotional care?
- Does gender influence how I balance intimacy and distance in my work?
- How does gender prescribe expression of emotion and styles of communication in professional relationships with families and colleagues?
- How do I manage disparities in gendered beliefs?
- Does this influence my readiness or reticence to hear what is being said: for example, to encourage the patient to be excused from family duties?

- How can I, as a woman, guard against assuming too much responsibility for patient care, or, as a man, guard against becoming too interested in technical aspects of care?

How do technology and policy changes help or hinder health care?

Threatened budget cuts have increased uncertainty about employment prospects, crucial research and the very survival of hospital units. This has often increased paperwork in a bid to prove efficiency, adding to work pressure. Cost cutting, specialisation and privatisation have strengthened the commitment to prioritise limited resources, redefining health care in a way often at odds with previous experience and training. Where decisions about prioritising resources and reformulating structures have included participants' views, uncertainty and stress levels have been reduced, although not eliminated (Jick, 1987).

Increased use of technology is reshaping care, limiting emphasis on the traditional skills of medicine, like eliciting illness narratives, understanding and responding to distress. Aggressive treatment methods have limited the opportunity to carry out tasks many professionals were trained for: support, care and containment. Having entered careers with an image of intimate patient care, we can find ourselves fitting and monitoring equipment which can break down or provide false alarms. Arguably nurses' roles have been most affected, requiring constant training and monitoring equipment which frequently needs updating (Fitter, 1987).

Obviously, as technology becomes more integrated with all treatment, this will alter. However, technology has introduced a more profound source of stress: we can now sustain life beyond the point where someone can be seen to have a meaningful existence. While doctors carry formal responsibility for decisions to withhold treatment, ongoing contact with patients and equipment raises personal, ethical and existential dilemmas about quality of life for all.

Can we avoid de-skilling the families we meet?

Traditionally, interactions with ill people and their families were understood as relationships in which information (symptoms) were presented to a professional. However, studies of doctor-patient communication suggests these encounters are a two-way process:

different styles of eliciting information result in different answers, and professionals are influenced by patients' expectations of such encounters (Heath, 1986; Radley 1994). In this way, we mutually determine what it is safe to say or hear, be this about sexuality, death or disfigurement.

Our behaviour is affected by our beliefs, which comprise a combination of personal, professional and institutional beliefs, and may vary according to gender, race, culture and work context, whether in the private or public sectors. On the one hand, where our beliefs seem similar to people we meet, we risk making assumptions unquestioningly. However, where they do not fit, our capacity to hear what is being said can be impaired. For example, beliefs and fears about blame may mean we cannot hear or appreciate the depths of a mother's experience of personal blame: similarly, blaming patients and families for responding too readily or too slowly to symptoms may reflect our tolerance for uncertainty rather than theirs.

This is particularly important where people come from a culture different from our own, where styles of relating are coded differently, and patterns of care, the meaning of illness and a life after death clash with our own avowed beliefs. For immigrants and refugees, people who escaped civil war and discrimination in their country of origin, concerns about fitting in with the host culture and fears of secrecy can make it difficult to say when the care provided is inappropriate, undermining or discriminatory. While interpreters can help us understand cultures different from our own, this can sometimes be experienced as insulting, and ignorance or lack of availability means we risk using interpreters allied to opposing factions. However, we can only construct a clearer understanding of what is needed and available by recognising and respecting, rather than denying, difference.

As health-care facilities easily disempower people and foster dependence, greater sensitivity needs to be paid to families' *values* to ensure these encounters feel less punitive, or unsatisfactory. Our attitudes to *obtaining help* from others affect how we encourage others to use professional services, community resources or self-help groups. This means understanding how we define *professional competence* and *success*: when we are unable to save a life, or alter symptoms, is this our own responsibility, and are we failures? If we can move away from viewing illness and dying as a failure, we may be better placed to help families to accept their situation. Reflecting on what we bring to the work can be invaluable, both personally and professionally (Addison *et al.*, 1993; Rolland, 1994). For example, it may be useful to recall a past incident in which we or our families faced serious loss or vulnerability, and ask: .

- What did I learn from that experience about dealing with loss and vulnerability?
- How has it influenced my ideas about: whether to be optimistic or accepting when difficulties strike; how much control my family has over life; what is normal; how helpful a spiritual life can be and what is normal?
- How has this affected the way I confront blame, guilt and personal responsibility in work with families?

Exploring these issues can help us to disentangle our beliefs. Connecting with personal struggles in confidence and trust can increase our understanding of others, and may enable us to review whether our beliefs fit with present circumstances.

Ill people are confronted with a barrage of apparent certainty. Despite uncertainties in health care, we seem to emphasise what is known rather than unknown. At one level this is comforting as most people want know they will be cured rather than hear apologies for what is not known. However, inevitably they will learn that the treatment for cancer, asthma or cystitis varies from unit to unit, or that alternative therapies are more effective than traditional medicine. As choice of treatment can affect life or death, we need to help families assimilate what this means, and avoid adding further to the myth of certainty by splitting professional opinion further. This means extending our tolerance for uncertainty, but requires an environment where we feel safe to acknowledge what uncertainty means to us (Mason, 1993).

Personal anxieties about health

Working with illness can increase our awareness of physical vulnerability, raising concerns about illness, loss and damage. In starting this work, I recall becoming preoccupied with my own health. Accessing our own experiences, whether this involves having 'been there' and facing life-threatening illness, the embarrassment at finding that preoccupations with health were unfounded, or the guilt of being healthy while others face death, influences the range of conversations we feel able to hold with others. While personal experience provides the special insight of a survivor, we may need to guard against identifying too closely and remaining locked into our own traumatic experience. Examining our own feelings is essential to ensure we can attend to what is unique about the family's narrative.

As non-medical professionals, it may be useful to desensitise ourselves to facing people in pain, who are scarred, disfigured, distressed or angry in a concrete way: by joining medical colleagues in ward rounds, watching procedures like dialysis, desensitising ourselves to needles, or even visiting the hospital morgue.

As importantly, we need to find ways of *acknowledging physical health*, of bearing the difference, dealing with feelings evoked by being able to walk on our own two legs, or to hold open a heavy door for those in a wheelchair.

Mirroring within professional systems

The authority afforded to doctors can evoke clashes between medical and non-medical colleagues which reflect earlier struggles with status and power, returning us to old patterns of parent-child or sibling relationships. Finding a way of sharing both the rewards and frustrations of the work can go a long way towards alleviating the potential for conflicts of this sort.

However, just as our behaviour impacts on how family members respond, so too our reactions may mirror what is happening to others. In particular, where the family faces issues too frightening to confront, these may be 'projected' on to us, so that we pick up and own issues that belong to the family.

CASE EXAMPLE

In the family discussed earlier, an escalation in Lan's cancer led to a case conference being called. The meeting was attended by highly competent professionals, some of whom had collaborated previously. What became apparent was how much confusion existed between the professionals: confusion about roles, the family's history and previous decisions. We seemed to flood one another with details of family incidents and treatment. The confusion and flooding was compounded by Lan's reluctance to face her illness and wish to exclude her extended family from future contact with her daughters, delaying the process of providing substitute care for her.

Our difficulty as professionals in facing the fact that, despite our efforts, the mother was dying undoubtedly contributed to the confusion. We were only able to move from conflict to greater collaboration by considering what information this process provided about the family. We discussed whether our confusion mirrored the family's confusion: about who belonged in the family, the illness and their future together. The flooding seemed to reflect Lan's sense of being flooded by cancer and how she in turn flooded her daughters with her anxiety. We found that each of us had crossed our professional boundaries with this family, be it moving furniture or working overtime. This had left us feeling overstretched, blaming and let down by the family and one another. Responding to all calls for help robbed us of the capacity to fulfil the roles we were trained for. Reconnecting with our competence enabled us to recognise the chaos with which Lan felt confronted, enabling more realistic plans to be made.

These issues can be addressed on an *ad hoc* basis, in consultation with colleagues, or in supervision groups. Such a consultant or supervisor may act as a role model, engaging in self-disclosure about professional and personal issues without crossing the boundary of what would constitute personal psychotherapy (Keith *et al.*, 1993).

While it is crucial that we avoid overburdening families, commenting on our reactions can have a powerful impact on what is said and heard. Bringing ourselves into the room in a non-judgemental way shifts the balance of power, enabling different conversations and insights to emerge. These may include comments like:

- I'm finding it difficult to concentrate. I wonder why that is.
- This seems strange to me. We seem to be joking about something very frightening.
- As a mother myself, I wonder if it is more difficult for mothers?

Whether individually or in teams, when difficulties arise, it may be useful to ask:

- What do our reaction tell us about this family's dynamics?
- How does the way we relate to one another reflect what is happening in the family?
- What clues does this provide about intervention?
- What new information have I learned from this family's way of coping with illness?

It is equally important to consider interactions between families and non-clinical staff on the unit . The receptionist's comment that a father we were seeing was the angriest man she had met alerted my colleague, Barbara Dale and I to what yet another professional consultation may mean for him, how helpless and de-skilled he felt, and how hard it was to trust 'experts' who could not cure his son. Talking with him about his expertise as a consumer of medical services, good and bad, helped him connect with his competence, and hear what we could offer.

How do we manage personal and professional boundaries?

Whether we live alone or not, we all have families. However, we are rarely helped to consider how we negotiate the boundary between our personal and professional lives. Medical professionals have particular decisions to reach in deciding how to respond when family members develop the symptoms they are trained to address, with some ignoring serious symptoms and others becoming anxious about minor problems. However, dilemmas about personal-professional boundaries may be equally problematic for all health professionals. As suggested by McDaniel, Campbell and Seaburn (1989), before treating family members we should consider:

- Am I adequately trained to treat this problem?
- Am I sufficiently objective to avoid giving inappropriate care or am I too close to give bad news?
- Will treatment complicate family conflicts?
- Would my family comply better with another professional?
- Can I let someone else care for my family?

As psychotherapists in particular, helping others put their experience of illness into words can alter our relationship to those topics, and may enable us to talk more openly about death. As parents, we may want to prepare our children for the possibility of our death, telling them who would care for them if we died, or preparing a living will. However, this evolves from a process our families are not part of. They may find it difficult to listen to reminders of illness, loss and disability, leaving us feeling alone and isolated. Jealousies can arise where families feel neglected while we provide others with the time, caring and intimacy that may be lacking in our personal lives.

It is uncomfortable to raise issues like this in the face of illness. At the same time, our need to share aspects of our day may increase, blurring boundaries. We may find there are times we distance ourselves from our own families to avoid facing the loss or isolation we experience at work, or that we seek support from our families that should be available at work. While each context has its unique requirements, in most settings, safeguarding time and space to address personal concerns can be crucial to negotiating the balance between our personal and professional lives.

Suggested guidelines

1. Space to process work experiences is crucial.
2. Discussions with our families of what the work entails can prepare us all for how we may be affected.
3. Integrating self-exploration in professional development and training normalises the need for personal therapy, counselling or group work.
4. Although outside consultants can offer greater objectivity, they can be scapegoated or experienced as distant and punitive when exposing painful issues. This may be less likely when the whole unit decides to invite such a person in.
5. Understanding personal experience can be invaluable, but we need to ensure this is not the only frame through which we construct our understanding of the work.

Conclusions

This chapter returned to consider the roles we play as professionals in health-care systems. Inevitably, we are affected by our encounters with each new family, influencing the evolution of ideas about how best to be of service to families facing illness: today's theories and recommendations may be different from what we suggest tomorrow. This does not render insights less valuable, but highlights what we, like each family, learn from every unique encounter.

Concerns raised about the quality of care available to all sectors of our community highlight the importance of examining how we manage our professional roles. Attending to the impact of the work on ourselves can provide insight into the patient/family's dynamics and as well as our own. Like the families we see, we, too, can inhabit two worlds, the world of health and the world of illness; we, too, are vulnerable to illness and loss. While providing medical treatment or helping others to put their feelings about illness into words changes our relationship to these topics, we may well be confronted with painful old wounds. To alleviate fears of fragmentation and retain our own coherence we can find our interactions with families controlled by our own attempts to avoid emotional collapse.

Although this chapter outlined the cost to both patients and professionals of distancing and depersonalising strategies, it is important to recognise just how fearful it can seem to embark on more intimate interactions. It is therefore important to ensure that any change in clinical work or training recognises the importance of providing the support central to maintaining our sense of coherence.

Summary

1. Work with physical illness can evoke powerful feelings of vulnerability in us all, influencing our personal and professional lives.
2. High levels of burn out are being reported amongst health professionals, affecting recruitment, training and clinical practice.
3. Changes in health care, including moves towards specialisation, privatisation, cost cutting and increased use of technology affect our work, impacting on job satisfaction and relationships with patients.
4. Training encourages us to distance ourselves from the impact of the work. However, the cost of trying to 'cut off' from feelings may increase rather than reduce stress levels.
5. Changes in clinical practice, selection procedures and training are required to reduce stress levels, with more effective supervision and feedback. The commitment of staff at all levels, and a collaborative work environment, are crucial to extending this understanding. Groups, individual supervision and ward rounds can provide a context for reflection, while ensuring this does not become psychotherapy.
6. Interactions within professional groups can mirror what is happening to the family.
7. Our encounters with families may be influenced by personal anxieties about health, experience with illness, and how loss and vulnerability were addressed in our family of origin.
8. We need to find ways of recognising this while safeguarding personal and professional boundaries.

9

Clinical Epilogue: A Family's Experience of Adjusting to the Loss of Health

by John Byng-Hall

This final chapter will start with a brief conceptualisation of how families adapt to their roles in chronic illness and how the professionals can help. It will then describe work with a family with multiple illnesses giving verbatim accounts of some of their experiences of illness, and how the professionals contributed to that experience. Clinical implications for practice are outlined.

Accepting that the illness is chronic

Families have ways of managing brief illnesses such as flu, and move automatically into their usual caring roles; of nursing, comforting, fetching and carrying, relating to the doctor, taking over the sick person's role, etc. This follows the family's *illness script* (Byng-Hall, 1995) based on handling many previous bouts of sickness. Family members come to expect certain roles to be adopted when a member falls ill, which becomes a self-fulfilling prophecy with each member quickly coming in on cue to perform the necessary roles. How do families make the necessary adjustments when an illness becomes chronic? The danger is that the family may merely continue the roles adopted for a brief illness, which it can be inappropriate to assume in the long term. Children, for instance, can be helpful for a limited time when someone is ill but they should not be asked to be permanent carers.

Delay in adjusting to the long-term implications can occur when there is a failure to acknowledge the seriousness of the illness; or when the prognosis is uncertain or fluctuating, as in multiple sclerosis. In contrast other families might move quickly into, and then continue, caring for the sick person in an intense way, as it can provide welcome closeness. This, however, may militate against the patient's struggle to be as independent as possible, because to get better may threaten the closeness. Members of the same family may react differently: for instance, one may get very close to the patient, while another may not seem to be taking it seriously and to be carrying on regardless.

Fighting the illness, versus yielding to its implications

It is important to recognise the potential value as well as the drawbacks of each of the above strategies. It might be important for a family not to be emotionally overwhelmed by accepting all the implications of a serious diagnosis all at once, to hold on to hope when things seem very serious, or to get on with normal routines as much as possible until it becomes clear what the long-term future holds. Sometimes it may also feel vital to rekindle an intense protective closeness even when the illness itself does not seem to justify it, as this may be the avenue for emotional support so desperately needed at that moment.

The balance between fighting against the illness and yielding to its implications can at times become dysfunctional. As professionals we need to work with the family's own pace as much as possible, while being prepared to try to shift the balance when what is happening seems to be inappropriate. Families that have given up trying because it seems too hopeless may need appropriate encouragement. In contrast, a family that holds on to hope by denying the seriousness of the illness to the extent that they do not ensure adequate medical treatment needs to have this pointed out, and may also need some help in mourning the loss of health.

Mourning the loss of a healthy future

Giving the family a diagnosis, and discussing its prognosis, can provide an opportunity to start helping its members come to terms with what has happened. This is achieved by grieving for the lost health of the ill member, and facing up to the restrictions and the sustained effort long-term care will entail. The family will then be free to work out the most effective way to manage the illness.

Grieving the loss of good health is a family affair as it affects not only the patient but all the rest of the family. Family members can help each other to grieve (Byng-Hall, 1991). Facing the stark contrast between the images of a bleak future and those of health can lead the individual eventually to give up the old image and replace it with the new reality. However, to hold in mind the incompatible images of health, and that of a future of illness, is painful: the temptation is to switch the focus of attention on to something else, or to fail to take the implications on board, which avoids the distress. It is easier to grieve if you feel safe enough to be sad or cry. What helps is to have someone to talk to who can empathise with the sense of loss and be there to comfort and support. The fear of collapsing in a sea of tears, and of no longer being able to cope, may then recede. The most available people to share this with are usually other family members; how to involve them is considered below. The professional should also be able to offer this supportive setting.

Helping families hear bad news

The patient may not be able to hear the details of a serious diagnosis and its prognosis at first. Even if heard, they may not be able to take the implications in at once, either through shocked disbelief, or sometimes by jumping to unnecessarily pessimistic conclusions. If a relative can be asked to be present to support the patient, and to be part of the discussion about what to do, it can help. This makes it more likely that the facts will be heard and retained, and makes the language and terminology of the realities of the illness available to the family. The patient does not have to explain it all afterwards to her family. Seeing relatives separately can sometimes put a wedge between the patient and the family by leaving the impression that there are certain topics that cannot be, or have not been, talked about. If the relative has heard what the patient has been told then those topics can be broached again at home. Some innovative clinicians make a recording of the interview and give the tape to the patient to listen to at home so they can discuss it together later. Offering a follow-up interview also helps.

How can we provide a setting in which families feel secure enough to listen and to ask questions, and feel that we have understood their fears and dilemmas? Sharing catastrophic news is uncomfortable. To empathise, we have to imagine what it must feel like to them to be receiving the bad news. It can also be distressing to be with a really upset person. Just like our patients, we ourselves have ways of reducing emotional discomfort. This is necessary to some degree, otherwise those working with loss would soon burn out. However, it is important to be aware of the ways that we screen out the pain, and to ask ourselves whether we inhibit the patient exploring uncomfortable ideas by the methods we use to reduce our own exposure. Do we, for instance, give minimum information and depart in a hurry? Do we avoid eye contact so as not to see the painful effect, or lean away showing that we are distancing ourselves from them? Do we interview in settings that are so exposed to distractions, or so public that no personal responses are possible? Indeed, can we bear to provide an intimate supportive setting in which patients are more likely to be able to get upset?

How illness scripts evolve across generations

Ways of caring for illness can be passed down the generations, either through *replicative* illness scripts in which similar patterns are repeated in the next generation, or through *corrective* illness scripts, in which the parents try to avoid the painful experiences of their own childhood by doing better than their own parents were able to do. Neither response may, however, be appropriate to what is happening now, but exploring new ways can lead to *innovative* illness scripts. A mixture of all three scripts can often be identified in what is happening currently in the family's illness script (Byng-Hall, 1995). It can be helpful to explore how past illnesses were handled in order to understand the current style of care.

CASE EXAMPLE

The family I am just about to describe give some useful hints about what to do and what not to do. They had to struggle with serious illness over four generations.

I have worked with the McLairs on and off since 1984, and continue to do so because of recurring medical crises. The original referral was made by Cynthia, aged 32. She said that the problem was that Bob, her husband and the father of their child Jamie, aged 3, was depressed and withdrawn. Bob had just left home because he could not cope with the fact that his son had myoclonic epilepsy with additional handicaps and a poor long-term prognosis.

In the first session with the family, Jamie curled up under the table and went to sleep. The parents told me their story. Cynthia had a stroke as a result of a brain haemorrhage when Jamie was six weeks old. This left her with right-sided weakness and some speech problems. Jamie's epilepsy was diagnosed when he was 5 months old. Bob had responded to this crisis by throwing himself into managing the household. Cynthia made a reasonable recovery from the stroke and began to take charge of Jamie. Suddenly the bubble burst and the realities of his son's future also hit Bob. He started to feel dead inside and withdrew. Cynthia could not get through to him and they had rows. This became so difficult that he left home for a while.

Helping to mourn the loss of health

In the second session I defined the issue as one of mourning. Each of them was at a different stage in the mourning process. I explained that the first response to serious illness is often one of disbelief and that it takes time to accept what has happened. We explored how Bob's initial concern had been with whether or not Cynthia would recover and how he had to deal with the practicalities, which meant that he had no space to think about the appalling news of Jamie's epilepsy. He coped by just carrying on. It was only when Cynthia started taking over the care of their son that Bob could afford to start facing what had happened.

Cynthia, too, had an almost impossible task in facing her stroke, and then her son's epilepsy. This was particularly devastating as she herself had been epileptic since the age of 7, although the illness was now well controlled by drugs. My way of helping them was to work with the couple so that they could support each other to face what had happened. As Bob regained his emotional equilibrium he was once again able to take his part in their mutual support.

Over the years following further physical illnesses, I have been very impressed with this family's capacity to cope with overwhelming problems, and their expertise in managing illnesses. Recently Cynthia asked if there was anything that she could do as she knew that I was involved in a project that was looking at the impact of illness on families. I asked if I could interview her and her mother, Una, about their experience of illnesses over four generations, so that we could learn something about how past illness influences what happens later, and how professionals might improve the way they try to help.

Una's father had had tuberculosis of the lung; Una had lupus erythematosus; Cynthia had childhood epilepsy, a stroke, and a brain tumour diagnosed during contact with me; while Jamie had myoclonic epilepsy which was recently relabelled the Lennox-Gastaut syndrome.

Tracing illness scripts down the generations

Una: My father had TB, but he had it very badly, and he was not expected to live and was in hospital. I was very young, about 3, when this happened, as far as I remember he was away from home for about three years. An operation that was experimental at the time was performed on him removing ribs and one lung, and so on.

Therapist: What do you remember of that?

Una: My sister [*who was four years older*] and I went away. My mother was dealing with it all herself. For a while we went to a Home somewhere. I think to leave my mother free.

Therapist: You were sent away?

Una: I think 'sent away' is a word that I now use to describe that. I do have a memory from being away. I remember walking in a crocodile on top of cliffs in a biting wind. That's all I remember of it actually.

Asking what people can remember of an illness can be helpful. The story of the cliff tops captured the essence of her experience of the separation.

Therapist: So, whenever Cynthia, or Jamie, has been in hospital that has been quite poignant for you?

Una: Lots of things, yes, are poignant for me . . . My mother was very dedicated to my father's welfare – and to us, but particularly to him. And when my own children were very young and they wanted to sit on his lap and have a cuddle she would often say 'Don't, you'll hurt him.' So this went on right through.

Cynthia: He had a footstool and I was encouraged to sit on the footstool when we used to listen to Tony Hackett on the record player. We had to. She'd tell us, my grandmother, to keep it low, keep it quiet and not too loud.

Therapist: Do you think she was overprotecting him?

Una and Cynthia: Right, yes. (*Both nod heads*)
Una: Well, it had to do with him straining his body. He had ribs missing and I vaguely remember my fantasy that he had a huge hole in his back.

The problem of how to protect ill people appropriately is crucial. Una's father was clearly frail, but keeping the sound down suggested protection that went beyond what was demanded by the TB. Sometimes family members are also protected from distress by withholding uncomfortable information.

One of Una's corrective scripts

Therapist: Having seen how your father's illness was handled as a child, do you remember thinking, 'I would not do that with my children?'
Una: Yes, I did actually. My mother never talked about things. Everything was done innuendo and it was done because she wanted to protect us [my sister and me] from things concerning my father. Being absolutely clear about things – that would have helped. It would have cast aside a lot of anxiety and fear.
Therapist: So what you really wanted to do was to make sure everything was open?
Una: Absolutely. All through, I have never not talked about things with my children. (*Cynthia nods in agreement*)

Overcorrection of a tendency towards secrecy might, however, involve the children being overburdened by information inappropriate to their age.

One of Una's replicative scripts

Therapist: If you were going to take an aspect of how your parents handled illness, what would it be?
Una: I think it taught me to fight, because my mother was a fighter and she fought to protect my father, my sister and me. I think you have to fight to some extent, probably more so now because of the lack of resources and our needs are so great.
Therapist: Can you remember instances of having to fight with professionals?
Una: I think one has to be not aggressive because that doesn't get you anywhere, but be assertive. I don't think professionals are always right. I'm an ex-professional [*town planner*], and I certainly

wasn't always right. I tend to think for myself, as well as listen to what they have to say.

Both Una and Cynthia had replicated and elaborated this capacity to fight for the best care for the family, but were well aware of the dangers of antagonising those who held the family's health in their hands. We should remember this dilemma and encourage families to ask for what they need so that they do not have to demand it.

Avoiding ignoring vague symptoms in the presence of stress

Una's lupus erythematosus

Una: It is now about twelve years old. It's not deadly, it's not awful. For a very long time I knew I had something wrong with me. I was a fairly busy person working full time, so I cut down a bit because I was so tired. I knew the fatigue I was feeling wasn't normal, the aches and pains and so on. My then GP put everything I ever said to him down to stress and I had to get over that. I felt awful becoming 'a menopausal neurotic woman', but I had to go back quite a few times. He said, 'What do you think is the matter? Do you think you've got leukaemia or something?' Well it hadn't occurred to me. I just felt really quite ill.

As a medically trained family therapist, I always take my patients' physical symptoms seriously and never try to explain them in terms of stress until they have been fully investigated. Even then I remain uncommitted unless there is also a convincing case for there being psychological causes. I have sent a number of patients back to referring physicians because the psychological story did not add up. A number of these eventually turned out to have organic lesions.

Una: Eventually I went to see a specialist but I was not told exactly what was wrong for years. It was, 'A bit of rheumatism. Yes – you have got dry eyes.' Only very recently have I had chest problems. I go to the Chest Hospital where I have an extremely good doctor. I now really have got hold of what's wrong with me. But it took years. I suspect middle-aged women suffer the most because I've heard people say, 'When you're young it's not so bad, but when you get middle aged and menopausal – and you've got stress too – then . . .'

The delayed diagnosis and then a lack of precise information made it more difficult for Una to deal with her own loss of health, and to take the necessary care of herself.

Exploring what may resonate across generations

Cynthia's childhood epilepsy

Una: Cynthia was seven when epilepsy was diagnosed. This is a time when children are moving a little bit away from the apron strings, and making friends and doing things. I think we felt more reluctant to let her do things on her own. As she grew a bit older we were terrified, we knew we had to let her do things on her own, but I was very scared all of the time because of all the hazards and the dangers of having a terrible attack.

Cynthia: That's one hell of a dilemma.

Therapist: So your family script told you that you must be her protector? But you knew that you also needed to give her independence?

Una: Oh yes. It was very hard at that time actually. We were seen by a doctor, because he felt we weren't letting her grow up. Even if she'd been a normal child at that age I wouldn't have let her do the things he said she should be doing. We felt he really didn't know what it was like to have a child with that sort of condition.

We need to be cautious about challenging what parents do with their children. One way of avoiding being seen as having given ridiculous instructions is to explore their dilemmas, in this case balancing the need for safety against the need for development of long-term independence. If clients know that we are aware of the risks involved, we can help them to decide on the balance between the various dangers.

Therapist: (*to Cynthia*) Do you think that story of how your parents protected you was important? What sort of impact did it make on you?

Cynthia: I've gone the opposite way with Jamie. I've let him try everything. We have taken him to Orlando and Paris Disney and abseiling. He rock climbs, he canoes. He goes with two adults one each side of him. But he does actually abseil on his own now. There's a rope and he's got a helmet on.

This is an example of the creative mix between a *replicative script* (to protect) and a *corrective script* (to expose the ill person to apparently dangerous situations), which together with some innovative thinking allowed for exciting, but safe, adventures.

The danger of making psychiatric diagnoses on past history of emotional problems

Cynthia's stroke

Cynthia: Jamie was six weeks old.

Una: It was a nightmare. We were in Gambia and there had been a phone call saying Cynthia had meningitis, and she was getting worse. Our flight was a day or two late. She came home from hospital very soon but was so ill that we knew she shouldn't be at home. Then we decided she had to be in the hospital so we put her in the back seat of the car and took her back. Then the controversy started. Was it psychological or not? Was it because she had been discharged when she really wanted to stay – and that sort of stuff.

Cynthia had had a disturbed period during adolescence which involved admission to a psychiatric hospital. This history probably contributed to the psychological explanation.

Una: Then I saw a registrar and I said to him, as fiercely as I could within reason, 'I honestly believe this is something quite serious like a stroke.' Then the next day a consultant said that she was too sick for any tests to be done, and that she had had a stroke, and they could do nothing then because she was too bad.

Cynthia: I think I was in a coma for five days.

Una: As she came round all she said, over and over again, was, 'Mummy, Mummy, I'm frightened – I'm so scared.' . . . I also had a fight with my boss at work because they wouldn't let me go to the hospital to stay, and she just kept calling 'Mummy'. I just walked out and came back about a week later – and still had the job. It was a bit of a battle. Everything was a battle at that time.

It is now widely recognised that children need their parents in hospital. However, this also holds true for very sick adults. We should remember that.

When to tell bad news sooner or later?

Jamie's epilepsy

Cynthia told us that she had felt that there was something wrong with Jamie from the start. At 5 months he was diagnosed as having myoclonic epilepsy with drop attacks and, later, Jacksonian fits and *grand mal* attacks. His development was delayed, but for most of childhood he was still gaining some skills, but he then started to lose some capacities.

Cynthia: We had suspected he was going downhill as all the fits increased in number and in type. About two years ago, I knew in my heart he was deteriorating. School had been very protective I feel. The reviews were incredibly positive and I just kept thinking they're not being realistic.
Therapist: So being overpositive was really counterproductive?
Cynthia: Absolutely. Yes, I felt it was wrong.

Professionals can also be overprotective. Giving reassurance in the face of worrying evidence to the contrary can leave clients feeling unsafe as they can lose confidence in their helpers.

Therapist: What do you think it would have been like if they had been pessimistic?
Cynthia: (*thoughtful*) I suppose if I hadn't had the tumour (*see below*) diagnosed at that time – and all the rest of it, I could've dealt with it; but I think they were protecting me rightly because I couldn't have coped with it at that point.

This illustrates perfectly the dilemma that professionals also face whether to tell bad news soon when patients may not be ready, or to delay, which may be worse. I remember a time when Cynthia was furious because the school was being more pessimistic than she felt was right.

Cynthia: Well, we have felt that when Jamie has fits he gets very close to death. There are times when we're sort of willing him to take that first breath in after a convulsion. Also we felt that he was coming out of them more obviously damaged. His speech was being affected. Mum's asked a couple of times whether he could die, and each time we were told, 'Oh, don't worry about it, it's very unlikely.' Then we met up with the professor and she asked him again, and he turned to me and said, 'Are you ready to hear the truth?' I told him, 'Of course I'm ready to hear the truth, I've been waiting to hear it from the word go.' He said, 'We suspect it's Lennox-Gastaut Syndrome and life expectancy will be shorter than normal. There is a chance he could die in a fit.' In my heart I've known that.

Una: I think it's neglectful not telling you. You'd be able to have apparatus ready, or you'd be a bit more alert. But you're not told because it would be too threatening and worrying.

Therapist: Do you think if they had told you that some time ago that you would have been devastated?

Cynthia: No, it's worse suspecting and not knowing. Because now when I leave him with people, they know, I tell them explicitly not to leave him unattended.

Usually it is better to give bad news early, but in a supportive way. Patients may temporarily block news they cannot take, but at least the information is made available so that they can use it constructively when they are ready.

Listening and giving patients space

Cynthia's brain tumour diagnosed

Cynthia: I developed symptoms. I had symptoms left over from the stroke, but the other side of my body started being affected.

Therapist: I remember when you were wondering whether to take them seriously or not.

Cynthia: Well I tend to ignore my own symptoms. Also there's a degree of fear so you don't want to go.

Here I remembered that I had helped her through her doubts and fears so that she could go to the GP. She had thought she might have multiple sclerosis.

Cynthia: I went to see my GP, and I sat down and said, 'Forget who I am, forget I have Jamie. Look at me as a different person. I'm giving you some symptoms and I want you to look into them.' He referred me to a neurologist who said 'Oh. It's nothing', but to keep me quiet he did an MRI and, lo and behold, there was a tumour there. He referred me on to a surgeon. He was sort of free. He was a very loud, very large guy who once took phone calls from the Press about a boxer who had suffered a haemorrhage when we were there. I just couldn't cope with it any more.

Una: There was this occasion when I was there, we had come to talk about the brain tumour but we could hardly talk about it without interruptions so we said, 'Take the phone off the hook and stop people walking in all the time.' It was a bit gruesome.

Cynthia had now learned to demand what she needed from a specialist. As few patients will do this professionals must see to it that a suitable context is provided for discussing frightening situations.

Encouraging family support during medical consultations

Una: Cynthia and I always go together for consultations. How many of us can remember when you've been to a doctor and are told something really serious but you cannot remember when you get outside what was said. It's largely because of that that somebody always goes in with her. Jock [Cynthia's father] is also very good and supporting, but he would prefer to stay outside on the whole. Brian, my son [Cynthia's older brother], although he lives away, comes along when things are really bad. I think being confronted with three people on the whole probably seems aggressive although it isn't intended to be.

We should remember that when families appear in force it usually means that they are frightened rather than on the offensive.

Recognising anger and assertiveness are better than self-pity and bitterness

Cynthia: When I first came to see you with my husband Bob, I sat in silence.

Therapist: I remember. You were sitting in that chair, Bob was here (*points to Una's chair*) and Jamie, aged 3, crawled under that table and had gone to sleep. So this is a very different person sitting there now (*looking at Cynthia*). I suppose that's another aspect of the whole process. People grow emotionally. What do you think? Do you think the challenges you've had to meet have been a part of that? How much do you think that you have been able to use your mother's style, and her mother's before her?

Cynthia: No. it wasn't automatic to begin with. It's when I've come up against problems the more competent I've got. I've come up against ignorance, but I tolerate it, I suppose.

Therapist: What you had to do was learn to be assertive when the experts were clearly not doing it right.

Cynthia: Yeah, I suppose that's true. I don't know if you grow emotionally. I belong to a parents' support group and I used to be terribly shocked. I used to think parents were terribly hard and I didn't like it. It worried me and I'm now ashamed to say I have hardened up over the years. I think you do get a bit bitter over the years because you are constantly fighting for something.

Una: Well, we always said we weren't bitter. I think I'm beginning to harden a bit. It's not the 'Why should this happen to me?' bit – it's the anger.

Cynthia: Yeah. You've got to get on with life – you've got no option. Somebody without a disabled child once said, 'You've got a disabled child, how do you do it? I couldn't do it.' I wanted to hit her, I really did. My answer was, 'You would do it, because if it happened to you you've got no other option.' I think it's a side of bitterness – hardness in a way.

Cynthia was referring to how a parent is compelled to find a way to care, and so does not have the freedom to chose. It does not then feel like being a hero.

Cynthia: It's anger that resources aren't more readily available, that you have to battle for them. Why should you have to battle for something that's rightfully yours?

Therapist: But in that sense the anger is a central part of your coping? You get angry because resources aren't there automatically, which drives you to get them.

Note how important it can be to direct the energy of anger into taking some action and not into unproductive self-pity. Remember this when patients seem to be bullying you to get something done – it is energy to harness, not to resist. We also need to recognise that, perhaps unfortunately, the chronically sick often have to actively mobilise the multiple care agencies involved.

The family's advice to professionals

Cynthia: It is important to always respect the knowledge that patients have about themselves, about their own bodies and their own children.

Una: Trust in us as parents, in what we say and to learn to communicate better. That's for the medical profession, they aren't the best of communicators.

Therapist: What about how to give a diagnosis?

Cynthia: It's very lonely to suspect that you or your child has something but no one is actually saying it. I think after we've been given the information we should be given time to sit there and ask questions at the time, because we were numbed by things. To then give another appointment, and to say 'Now that you know, what questions do you have?'

Una: I think doctors find it difficult.

Cynthia: I remember, he didn't make eye contact with me and I just kept thinking, Christ! Look at me! But he didn't – not once.

Una: I think he was a little cold and distant although subsequently he wasn't. I think he found it difficult to talk about it.

Una: Once Cynthia's operation was suddenly cancelled so we went to discuss why. The surgeon was sitting there writing. Eventually he looked up and said 'Yes?' We said, 'We've come to discuss your reasons for not operating', and he was very short. In the end I said very gently 'Well, is there something about us that offends you?' He then put down his pen and said 'Oh sorry, I've had a horrendous morning', and then he was all right. He actually told us he had just had a patient that died.

Sharing the source of his distraction helped to bridge the gap. However, to know that one of his patients had died was hardly reassuring! This finally convinced them that it was safer to see someone else. The communication style of this particular surgeon provides a useful object lesson on what not to do. Overall however, the family was positive about the caring professions. How often, though, do we only want to hear the complimentary things, and fail to elicit any criticisms which we need in order to learn?

I have described my own work with this family in more detail elsewhere, together with an account of how my own experiences of illness influenced it (Byng-Hall, in press).

Conclusions

When a chronic illness is diagnosed, families can be helped to accept what has happened and to grieve the loss of a healthy future. Giving the diagnosis can be a time to start this process. For this, it is important to provide a safe setting in which patients can hear what is said and ask questions, preferably in the presence of other family members. Exploring past experience of illness may be useful if problems arise. Sometimes old ways are replicated, and at other times attempts are made to correct what were felt to be past failures, but neither of these responses may be helpful in adjusting to what is happening now. Professionals may also be misled by the past history of the family, especially by a history of psychiatric difficulties or by current stress as an explanation of symptoms.

Families build up an expertise in the day-to-day care which professionals need to respect. Remember that a patient's anger can be more useful when directed towards getting something done, rather than in the form of bitterness and self-pity.

Summary
1. Help family members to mourn the lost health of their family:
    (a) provide a supportive setting for discussing the diagnosis;
    (b) be aware of the ways that you might use to avoid the distress of giving bad news;
    (c) involve other family members if possible;
    (d) give a follow-up meeting.
2. Develop good communications:
    (a) look patients in the eye when talking to them;
    (b) do not allow distractions during discussions;
    (c) when giving information – give time to let it sink in; allow questions;
    (d) listen carefully to their worries;
    (e) bad news should, when possible, be given earlier rather than later, and in a supportive context.
3. Respect a familiy ability to cope with the situation.
    (a) Follow the family's pacing when possible in the tension between fighting the illness and yielding to its implication. Intervene, however, if the balance is dysfunctional.
    (b) Respect the family's knowledge of symptoms, and their management skills.
    (c) Respond positively to their fight to get the best treatment.

ADDITIONAL INFORMATION

These are books that might stimulate discussions about facing a serious physical illness. In suggesting reading to family members, it is *essential* that the professional concerned read it first to consider whether the material is likely to be helpful at that stage.

General guide

E. Schlenther (ed.), *Reading Therapy for Children: A Bibliography for Hospital and Home* (Edinburgh: Library Association, Medical Health and Welfare Libraries Group, Reading Therapy Subgroup, 1992).

Books for adults to read with young children

Althea, *I Go to Hospital* (London: Dinosaur Publishing, 1977)
Like all the books in this series, uses clear pictures to prepare children for what to expect from illness and treatment. Describes the experience of a child going to hospital. For ages 4–8.

Althea, *I Have Cancer* (London: Dinosaur Publishing, 1989)
Picture book describing Ben's experience of leukaemia. Explains how he had to stay in hospital for a long time for tests and treatment and how he hopes his story will help other children. Provides additional information for parents. For ages 4–8.

Althea, *I Have Diabetes* (London: Dinosaur Publishing, 1983)
Picture book explaining what diabetes means. The girl in the story can become tired and ill when there is too much sugar in her blood. Outlines how, although she has to be careful about what she eats and have regular insulin injections, she leads a full and normal life. For ages 4–8.

L. Brazier, A. Trapp and N. Yates, *Simon has Cancer* (Newcastle-upon-Tyne: Victoria Publications)
Picture book sensitively detailing the experience of cancer for Simon, aged 10. The book provides factual information on the nature of cancer,

chemotherapy and its side-effects and describes Simon's return to school. For ages 6–10.

A. Civardi and S. Cartwright, *Going to the Hospital* (London: Usborne, 1992)
A picture book that describes how Ben goes to see the doctor who decides he needs an operation. Outlines Ben's experiences in hospital. For ages 3–6.

D. Kimpton, *The Hospital Highway Code* (London: Pan Macmillan Children's books, 1994)
An entertaining book for young patients. Recognising that a hospital introduces children to a different world with new words and new experiences, the book uses words and humorous illustrations to explain what can be expected (for example, blood test and anaesthetics). Could also prove valuable for explaining to children what a sibling or parent is likely to experience when admitted. For ages 5–13.

S. Kohlenberg, *Sammy's Mommy has Cancer* (New York: Magination Press, 1993)
Picture book that provides a straightforward story to help children understand and accept the changes in their lives when a parent is diagnosed with a life-threatening illness. Introduction offers suggestions for involving children in the joys and sorrows of good and bad days, with the intention of providing a sense of safety and encouragement at this frightening time. For ages 3–8.

G. Mercer and P. Dennis, *A Visit to Hospital* (London: Kingfisher books, 1992)
A picture book that provides information about a hospital, including admission to a children's ward, what to expect from medical treatment and an operation. For ages 3–8.

J. Viorst, *The Tenth Good Thing about Barney* (London: Collins, 1971)
Picture book that describes a child's experience of facing the death and loss of a pet, and his attempts to remember all that was special about Barney. For ages 3–6.

S. Varley, *Badger's Parting Gift* (1984) (London: HarperCollins)
A picture story to help children come to terms with death. After Badger has died, his animal friends remember his kindness. For ages 5–8.

Reading for older children and their friends

J. Little, *Mama's going to Buy you a Mockingbird* (Harmondsworth: Puffin, 1984)

Jeremy discovers his father has cancer and that he isn't going to get better. A sensitive account of the impact this has on his relationship with both his parents. Fiction for ages 10–12.

J. Gillespie, *Well, I'm still Here* (London: Pan Macmillan, 1993)
When 9 years old, Joanna has a tumour removed from her brain; 11 months later it grows back. It is removed again and she is given 6 months to live. Five years later, she wrote this account of how she and her family coped with her illness and her recovery. For ages 8–13.

M. Gleitzman *Two Weeks with the Queen* (London: Macmillan, book: 1995; play: 1994)
Colin refuses to believe his younger brother Luke is dying of cancer. He decides to write to the queen to ask for help. His journey to London leads him to meet a couple facing AIDS. A sensitive account that highlights the challenges illness in one sibling presents to another. Fiction, for ages 9–13.

S. Mayfield *I Carried you on Eagles' Wings* (London: Scholastic Children's Books, 1987)
Tony's mother is dying and he finds it hard to put a brave face on things, often wishing he could fly away from everything. His friend Clare dares to ask him about his mother and seems to understand. When Tony finds a seagull with a broken wing, he finds he can nurse it back to health. Slowly he begins to understand how death too can sometimes bring freedom. Fiction, for ages 12+.

I. Strachan, *The Boy in the Bubble* (London: Mammoths, 1993)
Adam was born with a severe immune deficiency. He has lived most of his 15 years in a bubble, and his friend Ann is forced to visit him with the rest of his class. Fiction, for ages 12+.

J. Ure, *One Green Leaf* (London: Corgi Freeway, 1987)
David has a tumour on one leg. This means he has to have it amputated. Describes the impact this has on his friends. Fiction, for ages 13+.

Reading for adults and carers

S. Butler and B. Rosenblum, *Cancer in Two Voices* (London: Women's Press, 1994)
An autobiographical account of the impact of one womans' deteriorating cancer on the life of both herself and her partner. Both authors were academics and writers, and the book provides a brave and sensitive account of the similarities and differences in their hopes and expectations.

S. de Beauvoir, *A Very Easy Death* (Harmondsworth: Penguin, 1969)
A moving record of the author's mother's death from cancer. It describes the agonies of a 'very easy death', the clinical humiliations of a proud woman, the unforeseen flashes of love and hostility at the bedside.

S. Drakulic, *Holograms of Fear* (London: Hutchinson, 1987)
A harrowing but courageous novel in which a woman waits in fear for a kidney transplant. The illness re-evokes memories of her painful childhood and relationships with her parents. it describes what the daily ritual of dialysis has meant to her, her will to fight and her attempt to fashion new lives from old against all odds.

B. Morrison, *And When Did You Last See Your Father?* (London: Granta Books, 1983)
Blake Morrison's memoir of his father is about loss, love and death. It is an attempt to answer the question of whether he ever knew his father properly and who he really was. Dissecting family relationships, the book provides an unflinching account of his father's pain, and the tasks required of his mother and himself as his father's condition deteriorates.

E. Segrave, *The Diary of a Breast* (London: Faber & Faber, 1995)
Sex, death, parties, hospital life, motherhood and thwarted literary ambition features in this disarmingly honest diary. It records Elisa Segrave's 9-month struggle against cancer, providing a deeply and seriously funny account of her fellow NHS patients and her own pain, deprivation and pleasure.

Information resources

BACUP
3 Bath Place
Rivington Street
London EC2A 3JR

Tel. 0171-608-1661

The British Kidney Patient Association
Bordon
Hants

Tel. 01420-2021

Cancerlink
17 Britannia Street
London WC1X 9JN

Tel. 0171-833-2451

Cruse Bereavement Care
Cruse House
126 Sheen Road
Richmond
Surrey TW9 1UR

Tel. 0171-332-7227

Heartline Association (for children with heart conditions and families)
Rossmore House
26 Park Street
Camberley
Surrey GU15 3PL

Tel. 01766-75655

Malcolm Sargent Fund for Children
14 Abingdon Road
London W8 6AF

Tel. 0171-937-4548

National Association for the Welfare of Children in Hospital
Argyle House
29–31 Euston Road
London NW1 2SD

Tel. 0171-833-2041

The Terrence Higgins Trust
52 Grays Inn Rd
London WC1X 8JU

Tel. 0171-242-1010

For a more comprehensive list of associations and self-help groups in Britain contract:

The British Medical Association
Tavistock Square
London WC1 H9P

Tel. 0171-387-4499

REFERENCES

C. Abraham and P. Sheeran (1993) 'Inferring cognitions, predicting behaviour: two challenges for social cognition models', *Health Psychology Update*, 14, 18–23.

R. B. Addison *et al.* (1993) Reflections on physical vulnerability: opening the dialogue *Family Systems Medicine*, 11 (1), 31–46.

F. Alexander (1950) *Psychosomatic Medicine* (New York: Norton).

J. Altschuler (1993) 'Gender and illness: implications for family therapy', *Journal of Family Therapy*, 15 (4), 381–402.

J. Altschuler, D. Black, R. Trompeter, M. FitzPatrick and H. Peto (1991) 'Adolescents in end stage renal failure: a pilot study of family factors in compliance and treatment considerations', *Family Systems Medicine*, 9 (3), 229–47.

R. Anderson (1987) 'The unremitting burden on carers', *British Medical Journal*, 294, 73–4.

A. Antonovsky (1979) *Health, Stress and Coping* (San Francisco: Jossey-Bass).

K. A. Applebaum *et al.* (1988) 'Cognitive behavioural treatment of a veteran population with moderate to severe rheumatoid arthritis', *Behaviour Therapy*, 19, 489–512.

M. Balint (1957) *The Doctor, his Patient and the Illness* (London: Pitman).

J. Ballenger and J. L. Alpert (1989) 'Family factors in the decision to seek Medical Care', in C. R. Ramsay, *Family Systems in Medicine* (London: Guilford Press).

O. D. Barbarin, D. Hughes and M. Chesler (1985) 'Stress, coping and marital functioning among parents of children with cancer', *Journal of Marriage and the Family*, 47, 473–80.

G. Bateson, 'Double bind' (1969), reprinted in *Steps to an Ecology of Mind* (St Albans: Paladin).

W. R. Beardslea (1989) 'The role of self-understanding in resilient individuals: the development of a perspective,' *American Journal of Orthopsychiatry*, 59 (2), 266–78.

H. Bequaert Holmes and L. M. Purdey (1992) 'Can clinical research be both scientific and ethical', in H. Bequaert Homes and L. M. Purdey (eds), *Feminist Perspectives in Medical Ethics* (Bloomington: Indiana Press).

M. Blaxter (1983) 'The cause of disease: women talking', *Social Science and Medicine*, 17, 56.

A. E. Blechman and A. M. Delamater (1993) in R. E. Cole and D. Reiss (eds), *How do Families Cope with Chronic Illness?* (London: Lawrence Erlbaum).

M. Bluebond-Langner (1978) *The Private Worlds of Dying Children*, (Princeton, NJ: Princeton University Press).

P. Boss (1991) Ambiguous Loss', in F. Walsh and M. McGoldrich (eds), *Living Beyond Loss* (London: Norton).

J. Bowlby (1988) *A Secure Base: Clinical Applications of Attachment Theory* (London: Routledge).

J. Bowlby and J. Robertson (1952) 'A two year old goes to hospital: a scientific film', *Proceedings of the Royal Society of Medicine*, 46, 425–7.

C. Burck and B. Speed (1995) *Gender, Power and Relationships* (London: Routledge).

M. Bury (1982) 'Chronic illness as biographical disruption', *Sociology of Health and Illness*, 4 (2), 167–83.

S. Butler and B. Rosenblum (1994) *Cancer in Two Voices* (London: Women's Press).

J. Byng-Hall (1991) 'Family scripts and loss', in F. Walsh and M. McGoldrich (eds), *Living Beyond Loss* (London: Norton).

J. Byng-Hall (1995) *Rewriting Family Scripts: Improvisation and systems change* (London: Guilford Press, 1995).

J. Byng-Hall (forthcoming) 'Recurring nightmares: heroic efforts', in S. H. McDaniel, J. Hepworth and W. Doherty (eds), *Stories of Medical Family Therapy: Towards the Practice of Collaborative Family Health Care* (New York: Basic Books).

D. M. Cadman, D. Boyle, P. Szatmari and D. R. Offord (1987) 'Chronic illness, disability and mental and social well-being: findings of the Ontario Child Health Study', *Paediatrics*, 79, 705–12.

D. Campbell, R. Draper and C. Huffington (1991) *A Systemic Approach to Consultation* (London: Karnac Books).

J. Carpenter and B. Onufrak (1984) 'Paediatric psychosocial oncology: a compendium of current professional literature', *Journal of Paediatrics*, 95, 119–36.

A. Charlton, D. Pearson and P. H. Morris-Jones (1986) 'Children's return to school after treatment for solid tumours', *Social Science and Medicine*, 22 (12), 1337–46.

M. A. Chesler, J. Allswede and O. Barbarin (1991) 'Voices from the margin of the family: siblings of children with cancer', *Journal of Psychosocial Oncology*, 9 (4), 19–42.

J. Claflin and O. Barbarin (1991) 'Does "telling" less protect more? Relationships among age, information disclosure, and what children with cancer see and feel', *Journal of Paediatric Psychology*, 16 (2), 169–91.

M. H. Cohen (1993) 'The unknown and the unknowable – managing sustained uncertainty', *Western Journal of Nursing Research*, 15 (1), 77–96.

L. Combrinck-Graham (1985) 'A developmental model for family systems', *Family Process*, 31, 139–50.

J. Cornwell (1984) *Hard Earned Lives – Accounts of Health and Illness from East London* (London: Tavistock).

B. Dale and P. Emerson (1994) 'The importance of being connected – implications for work with women addicted to drugs', in C. Burck and B. Speed (eds) (1994) *Gender, Power and Relationships* (London: Routledge).

Department of Health (1991) *The Welfare of Children and Young People in Hospital* (London: HMSO).

F. Deutch (1959) *On the Mysterious Leap from the Mind to the Body: A Study on the Theory of Conversion* (International Universities Press Madison).

S. Dhooper (1983) Family coping with the crisis of heart attack *Social Work Health Care*, 9, 15–31.

C. Eiser (1990) *Chronic Childhood Disease* (Cambridge: Cambridge University Press).

C. Eiser (1993) *Growing up with a Chronic Disease* (London: Jessica Kingsley Publishers).

R. K. O. Ell, H. Nishimoto, J. E. Mantell and M. B. Hamovitch (1988) 'Psychological adaptation to cancer: a comparison among patients, spouses and nonspouses', *Family Systems Medicine*, 6 (3), 335–48.

R. Emmanuel (1990) 'Psychotherapy with hospitalized children with leukaemia: is it possible?', *Journal of Child Psychotherapy*, 16 (2), 21–38.

I. Engstrom (1992) 'Psychological problems in siblings of children and adolescents with inflammatory bowel disease', *European Child and Adolescent Psychiatry*, 1 (1), 24–33.

C. A. Evans (1990) *Chronic Childhood Disease* (Cambridge: Cambridge University Press).

C. A. Evans, M. Stevens, D. Cushway and J. Houghton (1992) 'Sibling response to childhood cancer: A new approach', *Child Care Health and Development*, 18 (4), 229–44.

M. Ferrari (1984) 'Chronic illness: psychosocial effects in siblings – 1. Chronically ill boys', *Journal of Child Psychology and Psychiatry*, 25, 459–76.

J. Firth-Cozens (1992) 'The role of early family experiences', in the perception of organization stress: fusing clinical and organizational perspectives', *Journal of Occupational and Organizational Psychology*, 65 (1), 61–75.

M. Fitter (1987) 'The impact of new technology on nurses and patients', in R. Payne and J. Firth-Cozens (eds), *Stress in Health Professionals* (London: John Wiley).

P. Fonagy and G. C. Moran (1993) 'A psychoanalytic approach to the treatment of brittle diabetes in children and adults', in Hodes and Moorey (1993).

M. Foucault (1975) *Birth of the Clinic* (London: Tavistock).

M. Friedman *et al.* (1986) 'Alteration of type A behaviour and its effect on cardiac recurrences in post-myocardial infarction patients: summary results of the Recurrent Coronary Prevention Project', *American Heart Journal*, 112, 653–65.

N. Garmezy and A. S. Masten (1994) 'Chronic adversities', in M. Rutter, E. Taylor and L. Hersov, *Child and Adolescent Psychiatry* (Oxford: Blackwell Scientific Publications).

C. Gilligan (1988) 'The vulnerable and invulnerable physician', in C. Gilligan, J. V. Ward and J. M. Taylor, *Mapping the Moral Domain*, (Cambridge, MA: Harvard University Press).

V. Goldner (1985) 'Feminism and family therapy', *Family Process*, 24, 31–47.

S. Gonzalez, P. Steinglass and D. Reiss (1989) 'Putting the illness in it's place: discussion groups for families with chronic illnesses', *Family Process*, 28, 69–87.

H. S. Greenberg and A. T. Meadows (1991) 'Psychosocial impact of cancer survival on school-age children and their parents', *Journal of Psychosocial Oncology*, 9 (4), 43–56.

S. Greer and P. M. Silberfarb (1982) 'Psychological concomitants of cancer: Current state of research', *Psychological Medicine*, 12, 563–73.

T. Gualtieri and R. E. Hicks (1985) 'An immunoreactive theory of selective male affliction', *The Behavioural and Brain Sciences*, 8, 427–41.

J. L. Hafstrom and V. R. Schram (1984) 'Chronic illness in couples: selected characteristics including wife's satisfaction with and perception of marital relationships', *Family Relationships*, 33, 195–203.

R. Hale, R. and L. Hudson (1992) 'The Tavistock study of young doctors: report on the pilot phase', *British Journal of Hospital Medicine*, 47 (6), 452–64.

C. Heath (1986) *Body Movement and Speech in Medical Interaction* (Cambridge: Cambridge University Press).

C. Herzlich (1984) *Health and Illness* (London: Academic Press).

R. Hill (1988) 'Health and illness in Chinese society', in M. Kidel and S. Rowe-Leete, *The Meaning of Illness* (London: Routledge).

S. A. Hill and M. K. Zimmerman (1995) 'Valiant girls and vulnerable boys: the impact of gender and race on mother's caregiving for chronically ill children', *Journal of Marriage and the Family*, 57, 43–53.

M. Hodes and S. Moorey (1993) 'Mind, body and psychotherapies', in M. Hodes and S. Moorey (eds), *Psychological Treatment in Disease and Illness* (London: Gaskill).

W. A. Horwitz and A. E. Kazak (1990) 'Family adaptation to childhood cancer: Sibling and family systems variables', *Journal of Clinical Child Psychiatry*, 19, 221–8.

L. A. Huebner, J. A. Royer and J. Morrel (1981) 'The assessment and remediation of dysfunctional stress in medical students', *Journal of Medical Education*, 56, 547–58.

A. L. Hurtig and L. S. White (1986) 'Psychosocial Adjustment in Children and Adolescents with Sickle Cell Disease', *Journal of Paediatric Psychology*, 11 (3), 411–27.

E. Imber-Black (1991) 'Rituals and the Healing Process', in F. Walsh and M. McGoldrich, *Living Beyond Loss* (London: Norton).

M. Jacobus, E. F. Keller and S. Shuttleworth (eds) (1990) *Body Politics: Women and the Discourse of Science* (London: Routledge).

J. M. Jenkins and M. A. Smith (1990) 'Factors protecting children living in dysharmonious families: maternal reports', *Journal of American Academy of Child and Adolescent Psychiatry*, 29, 60–9.

T. D. Jick (1987) 'The hospital as a context', in R. Payne and J. Firth-Cozens (eds), *Stress in Health Professionals* (London: John Wiley).

H. Joffe (1994) ''Not me'', ''not my group'': cross-cultural social representations of AIDS', in P. Guareschi and S. Jovchelovitch (eds), *Texts on Social Representations* (Brazil: Vozes).

D. Judd (1989) *Give Sorrow Words: Working with a Dying Child* (London: Free Association Books).

L. Kaufman Cartwright (1987) 'Occupational stress in women physicians', in R. Payne and J. Firth-Cozen (eds), *Stress in Health Professionals* (London: John Wiley).

A. Kazak and G. S. Nachman (1991) 'Family research on childhood chronic illness: paediatric onclogy as an example', *Journal of Family Psychology*, 4 (4), 462–83.

D. V. Keith *et al.* (1993) 'A Balint-oriented case consultation group with residents in family practice: considerations for training and the doctor patient relationship', *Family Systems Medicine*, 11 (4), 375–83.

M. A. Keitl, M. A. Zevon, J. B. Rounds, N. J. Petrelli and C. Karakousis (1990) 'Spouse adjustment to cancer surgery: distress and coping responses', *Journal of Surgical Oncology*, 43, 148–53.

A. Kleinman (1988) *The Illness Narratives: Suffering, Healing and the Human Condition* (London: Basic Books).

G. Koocher and B. McDonald (1992) 'Preventative intervention and family coping with a child's life-threatening experience of terminal illness', in J. Akamatsu *et al.* (eds), *Family Health Psychology*, (Washington, DC: Hemisphere).

D. M. W. Kriegsman, B. W. J. H. Penninx and J. T. M. van Eijk (1995) 'A Criterion-based literature survey of the relationship between family support and incidence and course of chronic disease in the elderly', *Family Systems Medicine*, 13 (1), 39–68.

E. Kubler-Ross (1983) *On Children and Death* (London: Macmillan).

R. Lansdown and G. Benjamin (1985) 'The development of the concept of death and its relationship to communicating with dying children', *Child: Care, health and development*, 11 13–20.

R. Lansdown and A. Goldman (1991) 'Children with cancer', in M. Watson (ed.), *Cancer Patient Care: Psychosocial Treatment Methods* (Cambridge: Cambridge University Press).

R. S. Lazarus and S. Folkman (1984) *Stress, Appraisal and Coping* (New York: Springer).

R. E. Lee and T. Dwyer (1995) 'Co-constructed narratives around being "sick": a minimalist model', *Contemporary Family Therapy*, 17 (1), 65–82.

S. D. Llewelyn (1989) 'Caring: the costs to nurses and relatives', in A. K. Broome (ed.), *Health Psychology: process and applications* (London: Chapman & Hall).

F. M. Lewis, M. A. Hammond and N. F. Woods (1993) 'The Family's Functioning with Newly Diagnosed Breast Cancer in the Mother: The Development of an Explanatory Model', *Journal of Behavioural Medicine*, 16 (4), 351–370.

D. Lobato, D. Faust and A. Spirito (1988) 'Examining the effects of disease and disability on children's sibling relationships', *Journal of Paediatric Psychology*, 13 (3), 389–407.

P. Maguire (1985) 'Improving the detection of psychiatric problems in cancer patients', *Social Science and Medicine*, 20 819–23.

P. A. Marshall and J. P. O'Keefe (1995) 'Medical students' first person narratives of a patient's story of AIDS', *Social Science and Medicine*, 40 (1), 67–76.

B. Mason (1993) 'Towards a position of safe uncertainty', *Human Systems: The Journal for Systemic Consultation and Management*, 4, 189–200.

H. R. Maturana and J. Varela (1988) *The Tree of Knowledge* (London: New Science Library).

S. H. McDaniel, T. Campbell and D. B. Seaburn (1989) 'Managing personal and professional boundaries: How to make the physicians' own issues a resource in patient care', *Family Systems Medicine*, 7 (4), 385–96.

S. H. McDaniel, J. Hepworth and W. Doherty (1992) *Medical Family Therapy* (New York: Basic Books).

I. Menzies Lyth (1957) 'The functioning of social systems as a defence against anxiety, reprinted in I. Menzies Lyth, *Containing Anxiety in Institutions: Selected Essays* (London: Free Association Books, 1988).

I. Meyerstein (1994) 'Reflections on "being there" and "doing" in family therapy', *Family Systems Medicine*, 12 (1), 21–9.

A. Miles (1991) *Women, Health and Medicine* (Milton Keynes: Open University Press).

J. W. Mold and H. F. Stein (1986) 'The cascade effect in the clinical care of patients', *New England Journal of Medicine*, 314, 512–14.

B. Montalvo, and M. Elliot (1994) 'Assisting terminally ill patients and their families: an orientation model', *Family Systems Medicine*, 12 (3), 269–80.

S. Moorey (1991) 'Adjuvant psychological therapy for anxiety and depression', in M. Watson (ed.), *Cancer Patient Care: Psychosocial Treatment Methods* (Cambridge: Cambridge University Press).

B. Morrison (1993) *And When Did You Last See Your Father?* (London: Granta Books).

G. Parker (1993) *With This Body* (Milton Keynes: Open University Press).

J. Patterson and H. I. McCubbin (1985) 'Family Transitions: Adaptation to Stress' in H. I. McCubbin and C. R. Figley (eds), *Stress and the Family: Coping with Normative Transitions* (New York: Brunner/Mazel).

R. Payne (1987) 'Stress in surgeons', in R. Payne and J. Firth-Cozens (eds), *Stress in Health Professionals* (London: John Wiley).

J. M. Perrin and W. E. McLean (1988) 'Children with chronic illness: the prevention of dysfunction', *Paediatric clinics of North America*, 35, 1325–37.

N. Petticrew, N. McKee and J. Jones (1993) 'Coronary artery surgery: are women discriminated against?', *British Medical Journal* 6886 (306), 3–19.

A. Radley (1994) *Making Sense of Illness: The Social Psychology of Health and Disease* (London: Sage).

D. Reiss, S. Gonzalez and N. Kramer (1986) 'On the weakness of strong bonds', *Archives of General Psychiatry*, 43, 795–804.

C. K. Reissman (1990) 'Strategic uses of narrative in the presentation of self and illness: a research note', *Social Science and Medicine*, 30 (11), 1195–1200.

J. S. Rolland (1987) 'Towards a psychosocial typology of chronic and life-threatening illness', *Family Process*, 26, 203–21.

J. S. Rolland (1994) *Families, Illness and Disability* (New York: Basic Books).

J. Rolland (1994) 'Working with illness: clinicians' personal and interface issues', *Family Systems Medicine*, 12 (2), 149–69.

E. Rosenheim and R. Reicher (1986) 'Children in anticipatory grief: the lonely predicament', *Journal of Clinical Child Psychology*, 15 (2), 115–19.

R. Roy (1990) 'Consequences of parental illness on children: a review', *Social Work and Social sciences Review*, 2 (2), 109–21.

M. S. Sanger, D. R. Copeland and E. R Davidson (1991) 'Psychosocial adjustment amongst paediatric cancer patients: a multidimensional assessment', *Journal of Paediatric Psychology*, 16 (4), 463–74.

E. Segrave (1995) *The Diary of a Breast* (London: Faber & Faber).

M. Selvini Pallazoli, L. Boscolo, G. F. Cecchin and G. Prata (1980) 'The problem of the referring person', *Journal of Marital and Family Therapy*, 6, 3–9.

A. E. Slaby, and A. S. Glicksman (1986) 'Adaptation of physicians to managing life-threatening illness', *Integr Psychiatry*, 4, 162–72.

S. Sontag (1991) *Illness as Metaphor and Aids and its Metaphors* (Harmondsworth: Penguin).

B. R. Spaulding and S. B. Morgan (1986) 'Spina bifida children and their parents: a population prone to dysfunction', *Journal of Paediatric Psychiatry*, 11, 359–74.

A. Spirito, D. DeLawyer and L. Stark (1992) 'Peer relations and social adjustment of chronically ill children and adolescents', *Clinical Psychology Review*, 11 (5), 539–64.

H. F. Stein (1990) 'The story behind the clinical story: an inquiry into biomedical narrative', *Family Systems Medicine*, 8 (2), 213–27.

P. Steinglass and M. Horan (1988) 'Families and chronic medical illness', in F. Walsh and C. Anderson, *Chronic Disorders and the Family* (New York: Hayworth).

N. Tarrier and P. Maguire (1984) 'Treatment of psychological distress following mastectomy: an initial report', *Behaviour Research and Therapy*, 22, 81–4.

G. J. Taylor (1992) 'Psychosomatics and self-regulation', in J. W. Barrow, M. N. Eagle and D. L. Wolitsky (eds), *Interface of Psychoanalysis and Psychology* (Washington, DC: American Psychology Association).

K. Tomm (1988) 'Interventive interviewing: Part III. Intending to ask lineal, circular, strategic, or reflexive questions?', *Family Process*, 27 (1), 1–15.

D. C. Turk and E. Fernandez (1991) 'Pain: a cognitive behavioural perspective', in M. Watson (ed.), *Cancer Patient Care: Psychosocial Treatment Methods* (Cambridge: Cambridge University Press).

J. E. W. Van Dongen-Melman and J. A. R. Sanders-Woudsra (1986) 'Psychosocial aspects of childhood cancer: a review of the literature', *Psychology and Psychiatry*, 27, 145–80.

J. Vernick and M. Karon (1965) 'Who's afraid of death on a leukaemia ward?', *American Journal of Disease of Children*, 109, 393–7.

E. Waechter, M. R. Crittenden, C. Mikkelson and B. Holaday (1987) 'Concomitants of death imagery in stories told by chronically ill children undergoing intrusive procedure: a comparison of four diagnostic groups', in T. Krulick, B. Holaday and I. M. Martinson (eds), *The Child and Family Facing Life-Threatening Illness* (Philadelphia: J. B. Lippincott).

J. Waldron (1983) 'Sex differences in illness, incidence, prognosis and mortality', *Social Science and Medicine*, 17, 321–33.

G. Walker (1983) 'The pact: The caretaker-parent/ill-child coalition in families with chronic illness', *Family Systems Medicine*, 1 (4), 6–29.

G. Walker (1991) *In the midst of winter* (London: Norton).

M. Watson *et al.* (1991) 'Relationships between emotional control, adjustment to cancer and depression and anxiety in breast cancer patients', *Psychological Medicine*, 21, 51–7.

N. E. Waxler (1981) 'The social labelling perspective on illness', in L. Eisenberg and A. Kleinman (eds), *The Relevance of Social Science for Medicine* (Boston, MA: D. Reidl).

D. K. Wellisch, E. R. Gritz, W. Schain, W. He-Jing and J. Siau (1992) 'Characterizing the distressed daughter of the breast cancer patient', *Psychosomatics*, 33 (2), 171–9.

M. Whitehead (1988) *The Health Divide: Inequalities in Health in the 1980s* (Harmondsworth: Penguin).

E. Wilde McCormick (1988) 'Heart abuse', in M. Kidel and S. Rowe-Leete, *The Meaning of Illness* (London: Routledge).

S. M. Zarit, P. A. Todd and J. M. Zarit (1986) 'Subjective burden of husbands and wives as caregivers: a longitudinal study', *The Gerontologist*, 26, 260–6.

M. Zborowski (1969) *People in Pain* (San Fransisco: Jossey-Bass).

F. Zimmerman (1995) *Who cares? Gender, nursing and the experience of caring'*, (unpublished Master's Thesis, Tavistock Clinic).

Index